PENGUIN CLASSICS

SEA LONGING

Sea Longing

Compiled by SIMON WINDER

~ ~ ~ ~

PENGUIN BOOKS

For CFBW

PENGUIN BOOKS

Published by the Penguin Group
Penguin Books Ltd, 27 Wrights Lane, London w8 5tz, England
Penguin Putnam Inc., 375 Hudson Street, New York, New York 10014, USA
Penguin Books Australia Ltd, Ringwood, Victoria, Australia
Penguin Books Canada Ltd, 10 Alcorn Avenue, Toronto, Ontario, Canada m4v 3b2
Penguin Books (NZ) Ltd, 182–190 Wairau Road, Auckland 10, New Zealand

Penguin Books Ltd, Registered Offices: Harmondsworth, Middlesex, England

This anthology first published 1998
1 3 5 7 9 10 8 6 4 2

The Acknowledgements on p. 223 constitute an extension of this copyright page

Illustrations on p. 1 and p. 216 by John Spencer

Set in 10/12.5 pt PostScript Adobe Minion
Typeset by Rowland Phototypesetting Ltd, Bury St Edmunds, Suffolk
Printed in England by Clays Ltd, St Ives plc

Contents

Publisher's Note

The intention behind the *Sea Longing* compilation had been to create a sunlit, sand-between-the-toes obverse to the gloomy world of its predecessor *Night Thoughts*. For better or worse, however, *Sea Longing* fails to achieve this. Whether gazing from high cliffs or standing on a beach, the writers in these extracts are at best rapt, at worst fearful – overwhelmed on the margin between welcoming earth and implacable water. Predictably this is not a situation which improves on the High Seas. As a forum for magical description of moods, creatures and the world's wonders the sea is an astounding inspiration – with many such moments collected here – but it also *terrifies*, and is terrifying to a unique degree.

The effortless manner in which for writers the sea is both matter-of-fact and gaudily metaphorical is perhaps what is at the heart of this compilation. *Moby-Dick* is of course a gigantic heap of symbols but it is no less valid as the greatest of all 'adventure stories'. We love reading about sailors cast adrift in an open boat because they are battling with such a heaving, out-of-control cultural framework, but we also really want them physically to survive.

British writers tend to be enamoured of the sea's margins, American writers of the open ocean. It is hard to find any interesting reason why this should be the case, but Melville, Poe, London, Crane and Whitman thrive there and provide a tone of ecstatic adventure matched in Britain only by the Scottish exile Stevenson and the unlikely import Conrad. The magic of this aspect of Conrad's writing continues to lie in the access he gives readers to a naval imperial steam-powered world with a literary potential seemingly never noticed by its mainly British exponents. This is perhaps another 'hidden' theme of *Sea Longing*: the mismatch between literature and subject. The men and women who have used the sea are almost always a separate group from the men and women who write poems, novels and journals. The Congo River or the Eastern Isles have held the literary imagination throughout this century only because a Polish exile became a sailor, learnt English, joined the British Merchant Marine, settled in Britain, and became a great novelist. Most seas, peoples and islands at most times in their history are closed to the reader's imagination. *Sea Longing* celebrates the fragmentary glimpses we have but also implies the entire worlds we can never recall.

The organization of the pieces of *Sea Longing* could have followed several valid principles: 'distance from the equator' (from *Youth* to *Frankenstein*), 'height above/below sea level' (from Matthew Arnold on a cliff to a giant squid in the benthic depths), 'water temperature', 'size of waves', 'degree of absurdity' (from Darwin's crisply described kelp to Poe's giant Antarctic bear) but ultimately it was felt that a random sequence was incomparably preferable. Sometimes (as with the Fielding and Cowper) an obviously attractive pairing presents itself.

All textual notes have been dropped as the many different styles employed by Penguin Classics over the years are often incompatible and would have loaded this compilation up with an inappropriate gravitas. As with *Night Thoughts*, the hope is that this medley of fragments will make readers look again at some of the extraordinary things which lurk in the Penguin Classics list.

Simon Winder

Sea Longing

There go the ships and there is that Leviathan whom thou hast made to take his pastime therein.

Psalm 104, Authorized Version

. . . lingering only, as all must linger and gaze on a first return to the sea, who ever deserve to look on it at all . . .

Jane Austen, *Persuasion*

We left London in ballast – sand ballast – to load a cargo of coal in a northern port for Bankok. Bankok! I thrilled. I had been six years at sea, but had only seen Melbourne and Sydney, very good places, charming places in their way – but Bankok!

Joseph Conrad, *Youth*

Grande Isle, Louisiana

Edna Pontellier could not have told why, wishing to go to the beach with Robert, she should in the first place have declined, and in the second place have followed in obedience to one of the two contradictory impulses which impelled her.

A certain light was beginning to dawn dimly within her, – the light which, showing the way, forbids it.

At that early period it served but to bewilder her. It moved her to dreams, to thoughtfulness, to the shadowy anguish which had overcome her the midnight when she had abandoned herself to tears.

In short, Mrs. Pontellier was beginning to realize her position in the universe as a human being, and to recognize her relations as an individual to the world within and about her. This may seem like a ponderous weight of wisdom to descend upon the soul of a young woman of twenty-eight – perhaps more wisdom than the Holy Ghost is usually pleased to vouchsafe to any woman.

But the beginning of things, of a world especially, is necessarily vague, tangled, chaotic, and exceedingly disturbing. How few of us ever emerge from such beginning! How many souls perish in its tumult!

The voice of the sea is seductive; never ceasing, whispering, clamoring, murmuring, inviting the soul to wander for a spell in abysses of solitude; to lose itself in mazes of inward contemplation.

The voice of the sea speaks to the soul. The touch of the sea is sensuous, enfolding the body in its soft, close embrace.

KATE CHOPIN
from 'The Awakening'

' 'Tis the voice of the Lobster . . .'

' 'Tis the voice of the Lobster: I heard him declare
"You have baked me too brown, I must sugar my hair."
As a duck with its eyelids, so he with his nose
Trims his belt and his buttons, and turns out his toes.
When the sands are all dry, he is gay as a lark,
And will talk in contemptuous tones of the Shark:
But, when the tide rises and sharks are around,
His voice has a timid and tremulous sound.'

LEWIS CARROLL
from *Alice in Wonderland*

Whales and Grampuses

The calm of the morning reminds me of a scene which I forgot
to describe at the time of its occurrence, but which I remember
from its being the first time that I had heard the near breathing
of whales. It was on the night that we passed between the
Falkland Islands and Staten Land. We had the watch from twelve
to four, and coming upon deck, found the little brig lying
perfectly still, surrounded by a thick fog, and the sea as smooth
as though oil had been poured upon it; yet now and then a
long, low swell rolling over its surface, slightly lifting the vessel,
but without breaking the glassy smoothness of the water. We
were surrounded far and near by shoals of sluggish whales and
grampuses, which the fog prevented our seeing, rising slowly
to the surface, or perhaps lying out at length, heaving out those
peculiar lazy, deep, and long-drawn breathings which give such
an impression of supineness and strength. Some of the watch
were asleep, and the others were perfectly still, so that there was

nothing to break the illusion, and I stood leaning over the bulwarks, listening to the slow breathings of the mighty creatures – now one breaking the water just alongside, whose black body I almost fancied that I could see through the fog; and again another, which I could just hear in the distance – until the low and regular swell seemed like the heaving of the ocean's mighty bosom to the sound of its heavy and long-drawn respirations.

RICHARD HENRY DANA, JR.
from *Two Years before the Mast*

'Behold, the sea itself'

Behold, the sea itself,
And on its limitless, heaving breast, the ships;
See, where their white sails, bellying in the wind, speckle the
    green and blue,
See, the steamers coming and going, steaming in or out of
    port,
See, dusky and undulating, the long pennants of smoke.

WALT WHITMAN
from 'Song of the Exposition'

Rock Pools

It was down on the shore, tramping along the pebbled terraces of the beach, clambering over the great blocks of fallen conglomerate which broke the white curve with rufous promontories that jutted into the sea, or, finally, bending over those shallow tidal pools in the limestone rocks which were our proper hunting-ground, – it was in such circumstances as these that my

Father became most easy, most happy, most human. That hard look across his brows, which it wearied me to see, the look that came from sleepless anxiety of conscience, faded away, and left the dark countenance still always stern indeed, but serene and unupbraiding. Those pools were our mirrors, in which, reflected in the dark hyaline and framed by the sleek and shining fronds of oar-weed there used to appear the shapes of a middle-aged man and a funny little boy, equally eager, and, I almost find the presumption to say, equally well prepared for business.

If any one goes down to those shores now, if man or boy seeks to follow in our traces, let him realize at once, before he takes the trouble to roll up his sleeves, that his zeal will end in labour lost. There is nothing, now, where in our days there was so much. Then the rocks between tide and tide were submarine gardens of a beauty that seemed often to be fabulous, and was positively delusive, since, if we delicately lifted the weed-curtains of a windless pool, though we might for a moment see its sides and floor paven with living blossoms, ivory-white, rosy-red, orange and amethyst, yet all that panoply would melt away, furled into the hollow rock, if we so much as dropped a pebble in to disturb the magic dream.

Half a century ago, in many parts of the coast of Devonshire and Cornwall, where the limestone at the water's edge is wrought into crevices and hollows, the tide-line was, like Keats' Grecian vase, 'a still unravished bride of quietness'. These cups and basins were always full, whether the tide was high or low, and the only way in which they were affected was that twice in the twenty-four hours they were replenished by cold streams from the great sea, and then twice were left brimming to be vivified by the temperate movement of the upper air. They were living flower-beds, so exquisite in their perfection, that my Father, in spite of his scientific requirements, used not seldom to pause before he began to rifle them, ejaculating that it was indeed a pity to disturb such congregated beauty. The antiquity of these rock-pools, and the infinite succession of the soft and radiant forms, sea-anemones, sea-weeds, shells, fishes, which had inhabited them, undisturbed since the creation of the world, used to occupy my Father's fancy. We burst in, he used to say, where no one had ever thought of intruding before; and if the Garden of Eden had been situate in Devonshire, Adam and Eve, stepping lightly down to bathe in the rainbow-coloured spray, would have seen the identical sights that we now saw, – the great prawns gliding like transparent launches, anthea waving in the twilight its thick white waxen tentacles, and the fronds of the dulse faintly streaming on the water, like huge red banners in some reverted atmosphere.

All this is long over, and done with. The ring of living beauty drawn about our shores was a very thin and fragile one. It had existed all those centuries solely in consequence of the indifference, the blissful ignorance of man. These rock-basins, fringed by corallines, filled with still water almost as pellucid as the upper air itself, thronged with beautiful sensitive forms of life, – they exist no longer, they are all profaned, and emptied, and vulgarized. An army of 'collectors' has passed over them, and ravaged every corner of them. The fairy paradise has been violated, the exquisite product of centuries of natural selection has been crushed under the rough paw of well-meaning, idle-minded curiosity. That my Father, himself so reverent, so conservative, had by the popularity of his books acquired the direct responsibility for a calamity that he had never anticipated became clear enough to himself before many years had passed, and cost him great chagrin. No one will see again on the shore of England what I saw in my early childhood, the submarine vision of dark rocks, speckled and starred with an infinite variety of colour, and streamed over by silken flags of royal crimson and purple.

EDMUND GOSSE
from *Father and Son*

On the Seashore

About five o'clock, the tide being then low, we went out on our first zoophyte hunt. The littoral zone at Ilfracombe is nothing but huge boulders and jutting rocks of granwacke or clay slate, which when not made slippery by sea-weed are not very difficult to scramble over. It is characteristic enough of the wide difference there is between having eyes and seeing, that in this region of sea-anemones, where the Mesembryanthemum especially is as 'plenty as blackberries', we climbed about for two hours without seeing one anemone, and went in again with scarcely anything but a few stones and weeds to put into our deep well-like jars, which we had taken the trouble to carry in a hamper from London, and which we had afterwards the satisfaction of discovering to be quite unfit for our purpose. On our next hunt, however, after we had been out some time, G. exclaimed, 'I see an anemone!' and we were immensely excited by the discovery of this little red Mesembryanthemum, which we afterwards disdained to gather as much as if it had been a nettle. It was a crescendo of delight when we found a 'Strawberry', and a *fortissimo* when I for the first time saw the pale fawn-coloured tentacles of an *Anthea cereus* viciously waving like little serpents, in a low tide pool. But not a polyp for a long, long while could even G. detect after all his reading; so necessary is it for the eye to be educated by objects as well as ideas. When we put our anemones into our glass wells, they floated topsy-turvy in the water and looked utterly uncomfortable; and I was constantly called upon to turn up my sleeve and plunge in my arm up to the elbow to set things right. But after a few days, G. adventurously made a call on the Curate Mr Tugwell, of whom we had heard as a collector of anemones and he returned to me not only with the announcement that Mr Tugwell was a very 'nice little fellow', and with three treasures – an *Eolis pellucida*, a

Doris billomellata, and an Aplysia, the first of each genus I had ever seen – but also with new light as to glass jars. So we determined to dismiss our deep wells, and buy some moderately-sized jars with shoulders to them. We had before this found out that yellow pie-dishes were the best artificial habitat for Actiniæ.

It was a considerable stretch to my knowledge of animal forms to pay a visit to Hele's shop, which lies in a quiet pleasant little nook at the back of the dissenting chapel opposite Wildersmouth. Hele gets his bread now by collecting marine animals and sending them to Lloyd in London, and he has a sweet-faced intelligent daughter who goes out with him collecting and manages the stock on hand. The first time we went there, they had a fine show of the *Actinia crassicornis* and a Gemacea, some Holothuriæ (the first I had ever seen) and the green *Anthea cereus,* which was new to me. But I had a still greater addition to my knowledge when G. went to Mort Stone with Mr Tugwell and Mr Broderie and brought home several varieties of polyps, which I had gathered a very imperfect conception of from books – Tubularian, Plumularian and Sertularian – exquisite little Eolides, and some compound Ascidians. Indeed, every day I gleaned some little bit of naturalistic experience, either through G.'s calling on me to look through the microscope or from hunting on the rocks; and thus in spite of my preoccupation with my article, which I worked at considerably *à contre-cœur,* despairing of its ever being worth anything.

When at last, by the seventeenth of June both my articles were dispatched, I felt delightfully at liberty and determined to pay some attention to sea-weeds which I had never seen in such beauty as at Ilfracombe. For hitherto I had been chiefly on chalky and sandy shores where there were no rock-pools to show off the lovely colours and forms of the Algæ. There are tide-pools to be seen almost at every other step on the littoral zone at Ilfracombe, and I shall never forget their appearance when we first arrived there. The *Corallina officinalis* was then in its greatest perfection, and with its purple pink fronds threw into relief the dark olive fronds of the Laminariæ on one side and the vivid green of the Ulva and Enteromorpha on the other. After we had been there a few weeks the Corallina was faded and I noticed the *Mesogloia vermicularis* and the *M. virescens*, which look very lovely in the water from the white cilia which make the most delicate fringe to their yellow-brown whip like fronds, and some of the commoner Polysiphoniæ. But I had not yet learned to look for the rarer Rhodospermiæ under the olive and green weeds at the surface.

GEORGE ELIOT
from 'The Ilfracombe Journal'

The Fossil Whale

From his mighty bulk the whale affords a most congenial theme whereon to enlarge, amplify, and generally expatiate. Would you, you could not compress him. By good rights he should only be treated of in imperial folio. Not to tell over again his furlongs from spiracle to tail, and the yards he measures about the waist; only think of the gigantic involutions of his intestines, where they lie in him like great cables and hausers coiled away in the subterranean orlop-deck of a line-of-battle-ship.

Since I have undertaken to manhandle this Leviathan, it behoves me to approve myself omnisciently exhaustive in the enterprise; not overlooking the minutest seminal germs of his blood, and spinning him out to the uttermost coil of his bowels. Having already described him in most of his present habitatory and anatomical peculiarities, it now remains to magnify him in an archæological, fossiliferous, and antediluvian point of view. Applied to any other creature than the Leviathan – to an ant or a flea – such portly terms might justly be deemed unwarrantably grandiloquent. But when Leviathan is the text, the case is altered. Fain am I to stagger to this emprise under the weightiest words of the dictionary. And here be it said, that whenever it has been convenient to consult one in the course of these dissertations, I have invariably used a huge quarto edition of Johnson, expressly purchased for that purpose; because that famous lexicographer's uncommon personal bulk more fitted him to compile a lexicon to be used by a whale author like me.

One often hears of writers that rise and swell with their subject, though it may seem but an ordinary one. How, then, with me, writing of this Leviathan? Unconsciously my chirography expands into placard capitals. Give me a condor's quill! Give me Vesuvius' crater for an inkstand! Friends, hold my arms! For in the mere act of penning my thoughts of this Leviathan, they weary me, and make me faint with their outreaching comprehensiveness of sweep, as if to include the whole circle of the sciences, and all the generations of whales, and men, and mastodons, past, present, and to come, with all the revolving panoramas of empire on earth, and throughout the whole universe, not excluding its suburbs. Such, and so magnifying, is the virtue of a large and liberal theme! We expand to its bulk. To produce a mighty book, you must choose a mighty theme. No great and enduring volume can ever be written on the flea, though many there be who have tried it.

Ere entering upon the subject of Fossil Whales, I present my credentials as a geologist, by stating that in my miscellaneous time I have been a stone-mason, and also a great digger of ditches, canals and wells, wine-vaults, cellars, and cisterns of all sorts. Likewise, by way of preliminary, I desire to remind the reader, that while in the earlier geological strata there are found the fossils of monsters now almost completely extinct; the subsequent relics discovered in what are called the Tertiary formations seem the connecting, or at any rate intercepted links, between the antechronical creatures, and those whose remote posterity are said to have entered the Ark; all the Fossil Whales hitherto discovered belong to the Tertiary period, which is the last preceding the superficial formations. And though none of them precisely answer to any known species of the present time, they are yet sufficiently akin to them in general respects, to justify their taking rank as Cetacean fossils.

Detached broken fossils of pre-adamite whales, fragments of their bones and skeletons, have within thirty years past, at various intervals, been found at the base of the Alps, in Lombardy, in France, in England, in Scotland, and in the States of Louisiana, Mississippi, and Alabama. Among the more curious of such remains is part of a skull, which in the year 1779 was disinterred in the Rue Dauphine in Paris, a short street opening almost directly upon the palace of the Tuileries; and bones disinterred in excavating the great docks of Antwerp, in Napoleon's time. Cuvier pronounced these fragments to have belonged to some utterly unknown Leviathanic species.

But by far the most wonderful of all cetacean relics was the almost complete vast skeleton of an extinct monster, found in the year 1842, on the plantation of Judge Creagh, in Alabama. The awe-stricken credulous slaves in the vicinity took it for the bones of one of the fallen angels. The Alabama doctors declared it a huge reptile, and bestowed upon it the name of Basilosaurus. But some specimen bones of it being taken across the sea to Owen, the English Anatomist, it turned out that this alleged reptile was a whale, though of a departed species. A significant illustration of the fact, again and again repeated in this book, that the skeleton of the whale furnishes but little clue to the shape of his fully invested body. So Owen rechristened the monster Zeuglodon; and in his paper read before the London Geological Society, pronounced it, in substance, one of the most extraordinary creatures which the mutations of the globe have blotted out of existence.

When I stand among these mighty Leviathan skeletons, skulls, tusks, jaws, ribs, and vertebræ, all characterized by partial resemblances to the existing breeds of sea-monsters; but at the same time bearing on the other hand similar affinities to the annihilated antechronical Leviathans, their incalculable seniors; I am, by a flood, borne back to that wondrous period, ere time itself can be said to have begun; for time began with man. Here Saturn's grey chaos rolls over me, and I obtain dim, shuddering glimpses into those Polar eternities; when wedged bastions of ice pressed hard upon what are now the Tropics; and in all the 25,000 miles of this world's circumference, not an inhabitable hand's breadth of land was visible. Then the whole world was the whale's; and, king of creation, he left his wake along the present lines of the Andes and the Himmalehs. Who can show a pedigree like Leviathan? Ahab's harpoon had shed older blood than the Pharaohs'. Methuselah seems a schoolboy. I look round to shake hands with Shem. I am horror-struck at this antemosaic, unsourced existence of the unspeakable terrors of the whale, which, having been before all time, must needs exist after all humane ages are over.

But not alone has this Leviathan left his pre-adamite traces in the stereotype plates of nature, and in limestone and marl bequeathed his ancient bust; but upon Egyptian tablets, whose antiquity seems to claim for them an almost fossiliferous character, we find the unmistakable print of his fin. In an apartment of the great temple of Denderah, some fifty years ago, there was discovered upon the granite ceiling a sculptured and painted planisphere, abounding in centaurs, griffins, and dolphins, similar to the grotesque figures on the celestial globe of the moderns. Gliding among them, old Leviathan swam as of yore; was there swimming in that planisphere, centuries before Solomon was cradled.

Nor must there be omitted another strange attestation of the antiquity of the whale, in his own osseous post-diluvian reality, as set down by the venerable John Leo, the old Barbary traveller.

'Not far from the Sea-side, they have a Temple, the Rafters and Beams of which are made of Whale-Bones; for Whales of a monstrous size are oftentimes cast up dead upon that shore. The Common People imagine, that by a secret Power bestowed by God upon the Temple, no Whale can pass by it without immediate death. But the truth of the Matter is, that on either side of the Temple, there are Rocks that shoot two Miles into the Sea, and wound the Whales when they light upon 'em. They keep a Whale's Rib of an incredible length for a Miracle, which lying upon the Ground with its convex part uppermost, makes an Arch, the Head of which cannot be reached by a Man upon a Camel's Back. This Rib (says John Leo) is said to have layn there a hundred Years before I saw it. Their Historians affirm, that a Prophet who prophesy'd of Mahomet, came from this Temple, and some do not stand to assert, that the Prophet Jonas was cast forth by the Whale at the Base of the Temple.'

In this Afric Temple of the Whale I leave you, reader, and if you be a Nantucketer, and a whaleman, you will silently worship there.

HERMAN MELVILLE
from *Moby-Dick*

Mr John Lok's Voyage to Guinea

In the year of Our Lord 1554 the eleventh day of October, we departed the river of Thames with three goodly ships, the one called the *Trinity*, the other called the *Bartholomew*, the third was the *John Evangelist*, the first day of November at nine of the clock at night departing from the coast of England.

The 17 day in the morning we had sight of the Isle of Madeira, a long low land with a saddle through the midst of it, standing in two and thirty degrees: and in the west part, many springs of water running down from the mountain, and many white fields like unto cornfields, and some white houses.

The 19 day at twelve of the clock we had sight of the Canaries. Tenerife is a high land, with a great high peak like a sugar loaf, and upon the said peak is snow throughout all the whole year. And by reason of that peak it may be known above all the other islands.

Seven or eight leagues off from the river del Oro to Cape de las Barbas, there use many Spaniards and Portuguese to trade for fishing, during the month of November: and all that coast is very low lands. The fourth of December we began to set our course southeast. We fell with Cape Mensurado to the southeast. This cape may be easily known, by reason that the rising of it is like a porpoise head. Also toward the southeast there are three trees, whereof the easternmost tree is the highest, and the middlemost is like a high stack, and the southernmost like unto a gibbet. All the coast along is white sand.

On the fourth day of September, under nine degrees, we lost sight of the north star. We came to anchor three or four leagues west and by south of the Cape de Tres Puntas. Then our pinnace came aboard with all our men, the pinnace also took in more wares. They told me they would go to a place where the *Primrose* had received much gold at the first voyage, but I fearing a brigantine that was then upon the coast, did weigh and follow them. The town is called Shama, where we did traffic for gold, to the northeast of Cape de Tres Puntas.

They brought from thence at the last voyage four hundred pound weight and odd of gold, of two and twenty carats and one grain in fineness: also six and thirty butts of grains, and about two hundred and fifty elephants' teeth of all quantities. Some of them were as big as a man's thigh above the knee, and weighed about four score and ten pound weight apiece. These great teeth or tusks grow in the upper jaw downwards, and not in the nether jaw upwards, wherein the painters and arras workers are deceived. At this last voyage was brought from Guinea the head of an elephant of huge bigness. This head divers have seen in the house of the worthy merchant Sir Andrew Judde, where also I saw it, considering by the work, the cunning and wisdom of the workmaster: without such consideration, the sight of such strange and wonderful things may rather seem curiosities than profitable contemplations.

The elephant (which some call an oliphant) is the biggest of all fourfooted beasts, his forelegs are longer than his hinder, he hath ankles in the lower part of his hinder legs, and five toes on his feet undivided, his snout or trunk is so long, and in such form, that it is to him in the stead of a hand: for he neither eateth nor drinketh but by bringing his trunk to his mouth, therewith he helpeth up his master or keeper, therewith he overthroweth trees. Of all beasts they are most gentle and tractable, and are of quick sense and sharpness of wit. They love rivers, and will often go into them up to the snout, wherewith they blow and snuff and play in the water. They have continual war against dragons, which desire their blood because it is very cold: and therefore the dragon lieth in wait as the elephant passeth by.

Touching the manners and nature of the people, their princes and noblemen use to pounce and raze their skins with pretty knots in divers forms, as it were branched damask, thinking that to be a decent ornament. And albeit they go in manner all naked, yet are many of them and especially their women, laden with collars, bracelets, hoops and chains, either of gold, copper or ivory. I myself have one of their bracelets of ivory, weighing two pound and six ounces of troy weight, made of one whole piece of the biggest part of the tooth, turned and somewhat carved, with a hole in the midst. Some of their women wear on their bare arms certain foresleeves made of the plates of beaten gold. On their fingers also they wear rings, made of golden wires, with a knot or wreath, like unto that which children make in a ring of a rush.

They are very wary people in their bargaining, and will not lose one spark of gold of any value. They use weights and measures, and are very circumspect in occupying the same. They that shall have to do with them, must use them gently: for they will not traffic or bring in any wares if they be evil used.

At their coming home the keels of their ships were marvellously overgrown with certain shells of such bigness that a man might put his thumb in the mouths of them. In these there groweth a certain slimy substance which at the length slipping out of the shell and falling in the sea, becometh those fowls which we call barnacles. Their ships were also in many places eaten with the worms.

There died of our men at this last voyage about twenty and four, whereof many died at their return into the clime of the cold regions, as between the isles of Azores, and England. They brought with them certain black slaves, whereof some were tall and strong men. The cold and moist air doth somewhat offend them. Yet doubtless men that are born in hot regions may better abide cold, than men that are born in cold regions may abide heat.

RICHARD HAKLUYT
from *Voyages and Discoveries*

Facing West from California's Shores

Facing west from California's shores,
Inquiring, tireless, seeking what is yet unfound,
I, a child, very old, over waves, towards the house of
      maternity, the land of migrations, look afar,

Look off the shores of my Western sea, the circle almost
    circled;
For starting westward from Hindustan, from the vales of
    Kashmere,
From Asia, from the north, from the God, the sage, and the
    hero,
From the south, from the flowery peninsulas and the spice
    islands,
Long having wander'd since, round the earth having
    wander'd,
Now I face home again, very pleas'd and joyous,
(But where is what I started for so long ago?
And why is it yet unfound?)

WALT WHITMAN

Ulysses under way after leaving Calypso

    And now, rejoycing in the prosp'rous gales,
    With beating heart *Ulysses* spreads his sails;
    Plac'd at the helm he sate, and mark'd the skies,
    Nor clos'd in sleep his ever-watchful eyes.
    There view'd the *Pleiads*, and the northern Team,
    And great *Orion*'s more refulgent beam,
    To which, around the axle of the sky
    The Bear revolving, points his golden eye;
    Who shines exalted on th' etherial plain,
    Nor bathes his blazing forehead in the main.
    Far on the left those radiant fires to keep
    The Nymph directed, as he sail'd the deep.
    Full sev'nteen nights he cut the foamy way;
    The distant land appear'd the following day:

Then swell'd to sight *Phaeacia*'s dusky coast,
And woody mountains, half in vapours lost;
That lay before him, indistinct and vast,
Like a broad shield amid the watry waste.

ALEXANDER POPE

The Thames Estuary

The *Nellie*, a cruising yawl, swung to her anchor without a flutter of the sails, and was at rest. The flood had made, the wind was nearly calm, and being bound down the river, the only thing for it was to come to and wait for the turn of the tide.

The sea-reach of the Thames stretched before us like the beginning of an interminable waterway. In the offing the sea and the sky were welded together without a joint, and in the luminous space the tanned sails of the barges drifting up with the tide seemed to stand still in red clusters of canvas sharply peaked, with gleams of varnished sprits. A haze rested on the low shores that ran out to sea in vanishing flatness. The air was dark above Gravesend, and farther back still seemed condensed into a mournful gloom, brooding motionless over the biggest, and the greatest, town on earth.

The Director of Companies was our captain and our host. We four affectionately watched his back as he stood in the bows looking to seaward. On the whole river there was nothing that looked half so nautical. He resembled a pilot, which to a seaman is trustworthiness personified. It was difficult to realise his work was not out there in the luminous estuary, but behind him, within the brooding gloom.

Between us there was, as I have already said somewhere, the

bond of the sea. Besides holding our hearts together through long periods of separation, it had the effect of making us tolerant of each other's yarns – and even convictions. The Lawyer – the best of old fellows – had, because of his many years and many virtues, the only cushion on deck, and was lying on the only rug. The Accountant had brought out already a box of dominoes, and was toying architecturally with the bones. Marlow sat cross-legged right aft, leaning against the mizzen-mast. He had sunken cheeks, a yellow complexion, a straight back, an ascetic aspect, and, with his arms dropped, the palms of hands outwards, resembled an idol. The Director, satisfied the anchor had good hold, made his way aft and sat down amongst us. We exchanged a few words lazily. Afterwards there was silence on board the yacht. For some reason or other we did not begin that game of dominoes. We felt meditative, and fit for nothing but placid staring. The day was ending in a serenity of still and exquisite brilliance. The water shone pacifically; the sky, without a speck, was a benign immensity of unstained light; the very mist on the Essex marshes was like a gauzy and radiant fabric, hung from the wooded rises inland, and draping the low shores in diaphanous folds. Only the gloom to the west, brooding over the upper reaches, became more sombre every minute, as if angered by the approach of the sun.

And at last, in its curved and imperceptible fall, the sun sank low, and from glowing white changed to a dull red without rays and without heat, as if about to go out suddenly, stricken to death by the touch of that gloom brooding over a crowd of men.

Forthwith a change came over the waters, and the serenity became less brilliant but more profound. The old river in its broad reach rested unruffled at the decline of day, after ages of good service done to the race that peopled its banks, spread out in the tranquil dignity of a waterway leading to the uttermost ends of the earth. We looked at the venerable stream not in the vivid flush of a short day that comes and departs for ever, but in the august light of abiding memories. And indeed nothing is easier for a man who has, as the phrase goes, 'followed the sea' with reverence and affection, than to evoke the great spirit of the past upon the lower reaches of the Thames. The tidal current runs to and fro in its unceasing service, crowded with memories of men and ships it has borne to the rest of home or to the battles of the sea. It had known and served all the men of whom the nation is proud, from Sir Francis Drake to Sir John Franklin, knights all, titled and untitled – the great knights-errant of the sea. It had borne all the ships whose names are like jewels flashing in the night of time, from the *Golden Hind* returning with her round flanks full of treasure, to be visited by the Queen's Highness and thus pass out of the gigantic tale, to the *Erebus* and *Terror*, bound on other conquests – and that never returned. It had known the ships and the men. They had sailed from Deptford, from Greenwich, from Erith – the adventurers and the settlers; kings' ships and the ships of men on 'Change; captains, admirals, the dark 'interlopers' of the Eastern trade, and the commissioned 'generals' of East India fleets. Hunters for gold or pursuers of fame, they all had gone out on that stream, bearing the sword, and often the torch, messengers of the might within the land, bearers of a spark from the sacred fire. What greatness had not floated on the ebb of that river into the mystery of an unknown earth! ... The dreams of men, the seed of commonwealths, the germs of empires.

The sun set; the dusk fell on the stream, and lights began to appear along the shore. The Chapman lighthouse, a three-legged thing erect on a mudflat, shone strongly. Lights of ships moved in the fairway – a great stir of lights going up and going down. And farther west on the upper reaches the place of the monstrous town was still marked ominously on the sky, a brooding gloom in sunshine, a lurid glare under the stars.

'And this also,' said Marlow suddenly, 'has been one of the dark places of the earth.'

JOSEPH CONRAD
from *Heart of Darkness*

The Docks of London

'Whither, O splendid ship,' the poet asked as he lay on the shore and watched the great sailing ship pass away on the horizon. Perhaps, as he imagined, it was making for some port in the Pacific; but one day almost certainly it must have heard an irresistible call and come past the North Foreland and the Reculvers, and entered the narrow waters of the Port of London, sailed past the low banks of Gravesend and Northfleet and Tilbury, up Erith Reach and Barking Reach and Gallion's Reach, past the gas works and the sewage works till it found, for all the world like a car on a parking ground, a space reserved for it in the deep waters of the docks. There it furled its sails and dropped anchor.

However romantic and free and fitful they may seem, there is scarcely a ship on the seas that does not come to anchor in the Port of London in time. From a launch in midstream one can see them swimming up the river with all the marks of their voyage still on them. Liners come, high-decked, with their galleries and their awnings and their passengers grasping their bags and leaning over the rail, while the lascars tumble and scurry below – home they come, a thousand of these big ships every week of the year to anchor in the docks of London. They take their way majestically through a crowd of tramp steamers, and colliers and barges heaped with coal and swaying red sailed boats, which, amateurish though they look, are bringing bricks from Harwich or cement from Colchester – for all is business;

there are no pleasure boats on this river. Drawn by some irresistible current, they come from the storms and calms of the sea, its silence and loneliness to their allotted anchorage. The engines stop; the sails are furled; and suddenly the gaudy funnels and the tall masts show up incongruously against a row of workmen's houses, against the black walls of huge warehouses. A curious change takes place. They have no longer the proper perspective of sea and sky behind them, and no longer the proper space in which to stretch their limbs. They lie captive, like soaring and winged creatures who have got themselves caught by the leg and lie tethered on dry land.

With the sea blowing its salt into our nostrils, nothing can be more stimulating than to watch the ships coming up the Thames – the big ships and the little ships, the battered and the splendid ships from India, from Russia, from South America, ships from Australia coming from silence and danger and loneliness past us, home to harbour. But once they drop anchor, once the cranes begin their dipping and their swinging, it seems as if all romance were over. If we turn and go past the anchored ships towards London, we see surely the most dismal prospect in the world. The banks of the river are lined with dingy, decrepit-looking warehouses. They huddle on land that has become flat and slimy mud. The same air of decrepitude and of being run up provisionally stamps them all. If a window is broken, broken it remains. A fire that has lately blackened and blistered one of them seems to have left it no more forlorn and joyless than its neighbours. Behind the masts and funnels lies a sinister dwarf city of workmen's houses. In the foreground cranes and warehouses, scaffolding and gasometers line the banks with a skeleton architecture.

When suddenly, after acres and acres of this desolation one floats past an old stone house standing in a real field, with real trees growing in clumps, the sight is disconcerting. Can it be possible that there is earth, that there once were fields and crops beneath this desolation and disorder? Trees and fields seem to survive incongruously like a sample of another civilization among the wall-paper factories and soap factories that have stamped out old lawns and terraces. Still more incongruously one passes an old grey country church which still rings its bells, and keeps its churchyard green as if country people were still coming across the fields to service. Further down, an inn with swelling bow windows still wears a strange air of dissipation and pleasure making. In the middle years of the nineteenth century it was a favourite resort of pleasure makers, and figured in some of the most famous divorce cases of the time. Now pleasure has gone and labour has come; and it stands derelict like some beauty in her midnight finery looking out over mud flats and candle works, while malodorous mounds of earth, upon which trucks are perpetually tipping fresh heaps, have entirely consumed the fields where, a hundred years ago, lovers wandered and picked violets.

As we go on steaming up the river to London we meet its refuse coming down. Barges heaped with old buckets, razor-blades, fish tails, newspapers and ashes – whatever we leave on our plates and throw into our dustbins – are discharging their cargoes upon the most desolate land in the world. The long mounds have been fuming and smoking and harbouring innumerable rats and growing a rank coarse grass and giving off a gritty, acrid air for fifty years. The dumps get higher and higher, and thicker and thicker, their sides more precipitous with tin cans, their pinnacles more angular with ashes year by year. But then, past all this sordidity, sweeps indifferently a great liner, bound for India. She takes her way through rubbish barges, and sewage barges, and dredgers out to sea. A little further, on the left hand, we are suddenly surprised – the sight upsets all our proportions once more – by what appear to be the stateliest buildings ever raised by the hand of man. Greenwich Hospital with all its

columns and domes comes down in perfect symmetry to the
water's edge, and makes the river again a stately waterway where
the nobility of England once walked at their ease on green lawns,
or descended stone steps to their pleasure barges. As we come
closer to the Tower Bridge the authority of the city begins to
assert itself. The buildings thicken and heap themselves higher.
The sky seems laden with heavier, purpler clouds. Domes swell;
church spires, white with age, mingle with the tapering, pencil-
shaped chimneys of factories. One hears the roar and the reson-
ance of London itself. Here at last, we have landed at that thick
and formidable circle of ancient stone, where so many drums
have beaten and heads have fallen, the Tower of London itself.
This is the knot, the clue, the hub of all those scattered miles
of skeleton desolation and ant-like activity. Here growls and
grumbles that rough city song that has called the ships from
the sea and brought them to lie captive beneath its warehouses.

Now from the dock side we look down into the heart of the
ship that has been lured from its voyaging and tethered to the
dry land. The passengers and their bags have disappeared;
the sailors have gone too. Indefatigable cranes are now at work,
dipping and swinging, swinging and dipping. Barrels, sacks,
crates are being picked up out of the hold and swung regularly
on shore. Rhythmically, dexterously, with an order that has
some aesthetic delight in it, barrel is laid by barrel, case by case,
cask by cask, one behind another, one on top of another, one
beside another in endless array down the aisles and arcades
of the immense low-ceiled, entirely plain and unornamented
warehouses. Timber, iron, grain, wine, sugar, paper, tallow, fruit
– whatever the ship has gathered from the plains, from the
forests, from the pastures of the whole world is here lifted from
its hold and set in its right place. A thousand ships with a
thousand cargoes are being unladen every week. And not only
is each package of this vast and varied merchandise picked up
and set down accurately, but each is weighed and opened,

sampled and recorded, and again stitched up and laid in its place, without haste, or waste, or hurry, or confusion by a very few men in shirtsleeves, who, working with the utmost organization in the common interest – for buyers will take their word and abide by their decision – are yet able to pause in their work and say to the casual visitor, 'Would you like to see what sort of thing we sometimes find in sacks of cinnamon? Look at this snake!'

A snake, a scorpion, a beetle, a lump of amber, the diseased tooth of an elephant, a basin of quicksilver – these are some of the rarities and oddities that have been picked out of this cast merchandise and stood on a table. But with this one concession to curiosity, the temper of the docks is severely utilitarian. Oddities, beauties, rarities may occur, but if so, they are instantly tested for their mercantile value. Laid on the floor among the circles of elephant tusks is a heap of larger and browner tusks than the rest. Brown they well may be, for these are the tusks of mammoths that have lain frozen in Siberian ice for fifty thousand years; but fifty thousand years are suspect in the eyes of the ivory expert. Mammoth ivory tends to warp; you cannot extract billiard balls from mammoths, but only umbrella handles and the backs of the cheaper kind of hand-glass. Thus if you buy an umbrella or a looking-glass not of the finest quality, it is likely that you are buying the tusk of a brute that roamed through Asian forests before England was an island.

One tusk makes a billiard ball, another serves for a shoe-horn – every commodity in the world has been examined and graded according to its use and value. Trade is ingenious and indefatigable beyond the bounds of imagination. None of all the multitudinous products and waste products of the earth but has been tested and found some possible use for. The bales of wool that are being swung from the hold of an Australian ship are girt, to save space, with iron hoops; but the hoops do not litter the floor; they are sent to Germany and made into safety razors.

The wool itself exudes a coarse greasiness. This grease, which is harmful to blankets, serves, when extracted, to make face cream. Even the burrs that stick in the wool of certain breeds of sheep have their use, for they prove that the sheep undoubtedly were fed on certain rich pastures. Not a burr, not a tuft of wool, not an iron hoop is unaccounted for. And the aptness of everything to its purpose, the forethought and readiness which have provided for every process, come, as if by the back door, to provide that element of beauty which nobody in the docks has ever given half a second of thought to. The warehouse is perfectly fit to be a warehouse; the crane to be a crane. Hence beauty begins to steal in. The cranes dip and swing, and there is rhythm in their regularity. The warehouse walls are open wide to admit sacks and barrels; but through them one sees all the roofs of London, its masts and spires, and the unconscious, vigorous movements of men lifting and unloading. Because barrels of wine require to be laid on their sides in cool vaults all the mystery of dim lights, all the beauty of low arches is thrown in as an extra.

The wine vaults present a scene of extraordinary solemnity. Waving long blades of wood to which lamps have been fixed, we peer about, in what seems to be a vast cathedral, at cask after cask lying in a dim sacerdotal atmosphere, gravely maturing, slowly ripening. We might be priests worshipping in the temple of some silent religion and not merely wine tasters and Customs' Officers as we wander, waving our lamps up this aisle, down that. A yellow cat precedes us; otherwise the vaults are empty of all human life. Here side by side the objects of our worship lie swollen with sweet liquor, spouting red wine if tapped. A winy sweetness fills the vaults like incense. Here and there a gas jet flares, not indeed to give light, or because of the beauty of the green and grey arches which it calls up in endless procession, down avenue after avenue, but simply because so much heat is required to mellow the wine. Use produces beauty as a by-product. From the low arches a white cotton-wool-like growth depends. It is a fungus, but whether lovely or loathsome matters not: it is welcome because it proves that the air possesses the right degree of dampness for the health of the precious fluid.

Even the English language has adapted itself to the needs of commerce. Words have formed round objects and taken their exact outline. One may look in the dictionary in vain for the warehouse meaning of 'valinch,' 'shive', 'shirt', and 'flogger,' but in the warehouse they have formed naturally on the tip of the tongue. So too the light stroke on either side of the barrel which makes the bung start has been arrived at by years of trial and experiment. It is the quickest, the most effective of actions. Dexterity can go no further.

The only thing, one comes to feel, that can change the routine of the docks is a change in ourselves. Suppose, for instance, that we gave up drinking claret, or took to using rubber instead of wool for our blankets, the whole machinery of production and distribution would rock and reel and seek about to adapt itself afresh. It is we – our tastes, our fashions, our needs – that make the cranes dip and swing, that call the ships from the sea. Our body is their master. We demand shoes, furs, bags, stoves, oil, rice puddings, candles; and they are brought us. Trade watches us anxiously to see what new desires are beginning to grow in us, what new dislikes. One feels an important, a complex, a necessary animal as one stands on the quayside watching the cranes hoist this barrel, that crate, that other bale from the holds of the ships that have come to anchor. Because one chooses to light a cigarette, all those barrels of Virginian tobacco are swung on shore. Flocks upon flocks of Australian sheep have submitted to the shears because we demand woollen overcoats in winter. As for the umbrella that we swing idly to and fro, a mammoth who roared through the swamps fifty thousand years ago has yielded up its tusk to make the handle.

Meanwhile the ship flying the Blue Peter moves slowly out

of the dock; it has turned its bows to India or Australia once more. But in the Port of London, lorries jostle each other in the little street that leads from the dock – for there has been a great sale, and the cart horses are struggling and striving to distribute the wool over England.

VIRGINIA WOOLF

Shipbuilding

Sunday, June 30, 1754

The morning was fair and bright, and we had a passage thither, I think, as pleasant as can be conceived; for, take it with all its advantages, particularly the number of fine ships you are always sure of seeing by the way, there is nothing to equal it in all the rivers of the world. The yards of Deptford and of Woolwich are noble sights; and give us a just idea of the great perfection to which we are arrived in building those floating castles, and the figure which we may always make in Europe among the other maritime powers. That of Woolwich, at least, very strongly imprinted this idea on my mind; for, there was now on the stocks there the *Royal Anne*,* supposed to be the largest ship ever built, and which contains ten carriage guns more than had ever yet equipped a first rate.

It is true, perhaps, that there is more of ostentation than of real utility, in ships of this vast and unwieldy burthen, which are rarely capable of acting against an enemy; but if the building such contributes to preserve, among other nations, the notion of the British superiority in naval affairs, the expence, though very great, is well incurred, and the ostentation is laudable and truly political. Indeed I should be sorry to allow that Holland, France, or Spain, possessed a vessel larger and more beautiful

* [later renamed the *Royal George* – see following poem]

than the largest and most beautiful of ours; for this honour I would always administer to the pride of our sailors, who should challenge it from all their neighbours with truth and success. And sure I am that not our honest tars alone, but every inhabitant of this island, may exult in the comparison, when he considers the King of Great-Britain as a maritime prince, in opposition to any other prince in Europe; but I am not so certain that the same idea of superiority will result from comparing our land-forces with those of many other crowned heads . . .

In our marine the case is entirely the reverse, and it must be our own fault if it doth not continue so; for, continue so it will, as long as the flourishing state of our trade shall support it, and this support it can never want, till our legislature shall cease to give sufficient attention to the protection of our trade, and our magistrates want sufficient power, ability, and honesty to execute the laws: a circumstance not to be apprehended, as it cannot happen, till our senates and our benches shall be filled with the blindest ignorance, or with the blackest corruption.

Besides the ships in the docks, we saw many on the water: the yatchts are sights of great parade, and the King's body yatcht, is, I believe, unequalled in any country, for convenience as well as magnificence; both which are consulted in building and equipping her with the most exquisite art and workmanship.

We saw likewise several Indiamen just returned from their voyage. These are, I believe, the largest and finest vessels which are any where employed in commercial affairs. The colliers, likewise, which are very numerous, and even assemble in fleets, are ships of great bulk; and, if we descend to those used in the American, African, and European trades, and pass through those which visit our own coasts, to the small craft that ply between Chatham and the Tower, the whole forms a most pleasing object to the eye, as well as highly warming to the heart of an

Englishman, who has any degree of love for his country, or can recognize any effect of the patriot in his constitution.

Lastly, the Royal Hospital of Greenwich, which presents so delightful a front to the water, and doth such honour at once to its builder and the nation, to the great skill and ingenuity of the one, and to the no less sensible gratitude of the other, very properly closes the account of this scene; which may well appear romantic to those who have not themselves seen, that, in this one instance, truth and reality are capable, perhaps, of exceeding the power of fiction.

HENRY FIELDING
from *The Journal of a Voyage to Lisbon*

On the Loss of the Royal George (1782)
Written when the News Arrived

Toll for the brave – the brave that are no more –
All sunk beneath the wave, fast by their native shore –
Eight hundred of the brave, whose courage well was tried,
Had made the vessel heel and laid her on her side;
A land-breeze shook the shrouds, and she was overset,
Down went the Royal George, with all her crew complete.

Toll for the brave – brave Kempenfelt is gone,
His last sea-fight is fought – his work of glory done –
It was not in the battle – no tempest gave the shock,
She sprang no fatal leak, she ran upon no rock;
His sword was in the sheath, his fingers held the pen,
When Kempenfelt went down, with twice four hundred
    men.

Weigh the vessel up, once dreaded by our foes,
And mingle with your cup the tears that England owes;
Her timbers yet are sound, and she may float again,
Full charged with England's thunder, and plough the distant
    main –
But Kempenfelt is gone, his victories are o'er,
And he and his eight hundred must plough the wave no
    more.

WILLIAM COWPER

Diving

Look into thought and say what dost thou see;
   Dive, be not fearful how dark the waves flow;
Sing through the surge, and bring pearls up to me;
   Deeper, ay, deeper; the fairest lie low.

'I have dived, I have sought them, but none have I found;
   In the gloom that closed o'er me no form floated by;
As I sank through the void depths, so black and profound,
   How dim died the sun and how far hung the sky!

'What had I given to hear the soft sweep
   Of a breeze bearing life through that vast realm of death!
Thoughts were untroubled and dreams were asleep:
   The spirit lay dreadless and hopeless beneath.'

CHARLOTTE BRONTË

'Full fathom five thy father lies'

Full fathom five thy father lies,
　　Of his bones are coral made;
Those are pearls that were his eyes;
　　Nothing of him that doth fade,
But doth suffer a sea-change
Into something rich and strange.
Sea-nymphs hourly ring his knell:
　　Ding-dong.
Hark! Now I hear them – Ding-dong bell.

WILLIAM SHAKESPEARE
from *The Tempest*, I, 2

The World below the Brine

The world below the brine,
Forests at the bottom of the sea, the branches and leaves,
Sea-lettuce, vast lichens, strange flowers and seeds, the thick
　　tangle, openings, and pink turf,
Different colors, pale gray and green, purple, white, and gold,
　　the play of light through the water,
Dumb swimmers there among the rocks, coral, gluten, grass,
　　rushes, and the aliment of the swimmers,
Sluggish existences grazing there suspended, or slowly
　　crawling close to the bottom,
The sperm-whale at the surface blowing air and spray, or
　　disporting with his flukes,
The leaden-eyed shark, the walrus, the turtle, the hairy
　　sea-leopard, and the sting-ray,

Passions there, wars, pursuits, tribes, sight in those
    ocean-depths, breathing that thick-breathing air, as so
    many do,
The change thence to the sight here, and to the subtle air
    breathed by beings like us who walk this sphere,
The change onward from ours to that of beings who walk
    other spheres.

WALT WHITMAN

The Fish, the Man, and the Spirit

To Fish

You strange, astonish'd-looking, angle-faced,
    Dreary-mouth'd, gaping wretches of the sea,
    Gulping salt-water everlastingly,
Cold-blooded, though with red your blood be graced,
And mute, though dwellers in the roaring waste;
    And you, all shapes beside, that fishy be, –
    Some round, some flat, some long, all devilry,
Legless, unloving, infamously chaste: –

O scaly, slippery, wet, swift, staring wights,
    What is't ye do? what life lead? eh, dull goggles?
How do ye vary your vile days and nights?
    How pass your Sundays? Are ye still but joggles
In ceaseless wash? Still nought but gapes and bites,
    And drinks, and stares, diversified with boggles?

A Fish Answers

Amazing monster! that, for aught I know,
　　With the first sight of thee didst make our race
　　Forever stare! O flat and shocking face,
Grimly divided from the breast below!
Thou that on dry land horribly dost go
　　With a split body and most ridiculous pace,
　　Prong after prong, disgracer of all grace,
Long-useless-finned, hair'd, upright, unwet, slow!

O breather of unbreathable, sword-sharp air,
　　How canst exist? How bear thyself, thou dry
And dreary sloth? What particle canst share
　　Of the only blessed life, the watery?
I sometimes see of ye an actual *pair*
　　Go by! link'd fin by fin! most odiously.

The Fish turns into a Man, and then into a Spirit,
and again speaks

Indulge thy smiling scorn, if smiling still,
　　O man! and loathe, but with a sort of love:
　　For difference must its use by difference prove,
And, in sweet clang, the spheres with music fill.
One of the spirits am I, that at his will
　　Live in whate'er has life – fish, eagle, dove –
　　No hate, no pride, beneath nought, nor above,
A visitor of the rounds of God's sweet skill.

Man's life is warm, glad, sad, 'twixt loves and graves,
　Boundless in hope, honour'd with pangs austere,
Heaven-gazing; and his angel-wings he craves:
　The fish is swift, small-needing, vague yet clear,
A cold, sweet, silver life, wrapp'd in round waves,
　Quicken'd with touches of transporting fear.

LEIGH HUNT

Zoophytes

In Tierra del Fuego, as well as at the Falkland Islands, I made many observations on the lower marine animals, but they are of little general interest. I will only mention one class of facts, relating to certain zoophytes in the more highly organized division of that class. Several genera (*flustra, eschara, cellaria, crisia,* and others) agree in having singular moveable organs, like those of *Flustra avicularia* (found in the European seas), attached to their cells. The organ, in the greater number of cases, very closely resembles the head of a vulture; but the lower mandible can be opened much wider, so as to form even a straight line with the upper. The head itself possesses considerable powers of movement, by means of a short neck. In one zoophyte the head itself was fixed, but the lower jaw free: in another it was replaced by a triangular hood, with a beautifully fitted trap-door, which evidently answered to the lower mandible. A species of stony eschara had a structure somewhat similar. In the greater number of species, each shell was provided with one head, but in others each had two.

The young cells at the end of the branches necessarily contained quite immature polypi, yet the vulture-heads attached to them, though small, were in every respect perfect. When the polypus was removed by a needle from any of the cells, these organs did not appear in the least affected. When one of the latter was cut off from a cell, the lower mandible retained its power of opening and closing. Perhaps the most singular part of their structure is, that when there were more rows of cells than two, both in a Flustra and an Eschara, the central cells were furnished with these appendages, of only one-fourth the size of the lateral ones. Their movements varied according to the species: – in some I never saw the least motion; while others, with the lower mandible generally wide open, oscillated backwards and forwards at the rate of about five seconds each turn; others moved rapidly and by starts. When touched with a needle the beak generally seized the point so firmly, that the whole branch might be shaken.

These bodies have no relation whatever with the production of the gemmules. I could not trace any connexion between them and the polypus. From their formation being completed before that of the latter; from the independence of their movements; from the difference of their size in different parts of the branch; I have little doubt that in their functions they are related rather to the axis than to any of the polypi. In a similar manner, the fleshy appendage at the extremity of the sea-pen forms part of the zoophyte as a whole, as much as the roots of a tree do of the whole and not of the individual buds. Without doubt this is a very curious variation in the structure of a zoophyte: for the growing part in most other cases does not manifest the least irritability or power of movement.

I will mention one other kind of structure quite as anomalous. A small and elegant Crisia is furnished, at the corner of each cell, with a long and slightly-curved bristle, which is fixed at the lower end by a joint. It terminates in the finest point, and has its outer or convex side serrated with delicate teeth or notches. Having placed a *small* piece of a branch under the microscope, I was exceedingly surprised to see it suddenly start from the field of vision by the movement of these bristles, which acted as oars. Irritation generally produced this motion, but not always. When the coralline was laid flat on that side from which the toothed bristles projected, they were necessarily all pressed together and entangled. This scarcely ever failed to excite a considerable movement among them, and evidently with the object of freeing themselves. In a small piece, which was taken out of water and placed on blotting-paper, the movement of these organs was clearly visible for a few seconds by the naked eye.

CHARLES DARWIN
from *Voyage of the* Beagle

The Ship Rats

'Then, on a fine moonlight night, all the rats left the ship.

'We had been infested with them. They had destroyed our sails, consumed more stores than the crew, affably shared our beds and our dangers, and now, when the ship was made sea-worthy, concluded to clear out. I called Mahon to enjoy the spectacle. Rat after rat appeared on our rail, took a last look over his shoulder, and leaped with a hollow thud into the empty hulk. We tried to count them, but soon lost the tale. Mahon said: "Well, well! don't talk to me about the intelligence of rats. They ought to have left before, when we had that narrow squeak from foundering. There you have the proof how silly is the superstition about them. They leave a good ship for an old rotten hulk, where there is nothing to eat, too, the fools! . . . I don't believe they know what is safe or what is good for them, any more than you or I."

'And after some more talk we agreed that the wisdom of rats had been grossly overrated, being in fact no greater than that of men.'

JOSEPH CONRAD
from *Youth*

The Wreck of the Hesperus

It was the schooner Hesperus,
    That sailed the wintry sea;
And the skipper had taken his little daughter,
    To bear him company.

Blue were her eyes as the fairy-flax,
    Her cheeks like the dawn of day,
And her bosom white as the hawthorn buds,
    That ope in the month of May.

The skipper he stood beside the helm,
    His pipe was in his mouth,
And he watched how the veering flaw did blow
    The smoke now West, now South.

Then up and spake an old Sailor,
    Had sailed to the Spanish Main,
'I pray thee, put into yonder port,
    For I fear a hurricane.

'Last night, the moon had a golden ring,
    And to-night no moon we see!'
The skipper, he blew a whiff from his pipe,
    And a scornful laugh laughed he.

Colder and louder blew the wind,
    A gale from the Northeast,
The snow fell hissing in the brine,
    And the billows frothed like yeast.

Down came the storm, and smote amain
   The vessel in its strength;
She shuddered and paused, like a frighted steed,
   Then leaped her cable's length.

'Come hither! come hither! my little daughter,
   And do not tremble so;
For I can weather the roughest gale
   That ever wind did blow.'

He wrapped her warm in his seaman's coat
   Against the stinging blast;
He cut a rope from a broken spar,
   And bound her to the mast.

'O father! I hear the church-bells ring,
   Oh say, what may it be?'
' 'T is a fog-bell on a rock-bound coast!' –
   And he steered for the open sea.

'O father! I hear the sound of guns,
   Oh say, what may it be?'
'Some ship in distress, that cannot live
   In such an angry sea!'

'O father! I see a gleaming light,
   O say, what may it be?'
But the father answered never a word,
   A frozen corpse was he.

Lashed to the helm, all stiff and stark,
   With his face turned to the skies,
The lantern gleamed through the gleaming snow
   On his fixed and glassy eyes.

Then the maiden clasped her hands and prayed
    That saved she might be;
And she thought of Christ, who stilled the wave,
    On the Lake of Galilee.

And fast through the midnight dark and drear,
    Through the whistling sleet and snow,
Like a sheeted ghost, the vessel swept
    Tow'rds the reef of Norman's Woe.

And ever the fitful gusts between
    A sound came from the land;
It was the sound of the trampling surf
    On the rocks and the hard sea-sand.

The breakers were right beneath her bows,
    She drifted a dreary wreck,
And a whooping billow swept the crew
    Like icicles from her deck.

She struck where the white and fleecy waves
    Looked soft as carded wool,
But the cruel rocks, they gored her side
    Like the horns of an angry bull.

Her rattling shrouds, all sheathed in ice,
    With her masts went by the board;
Like a vessel of glass, she stove and sank,
    Ho! ho! the breakers roared!

At daybreak, on the bleak sea-beach,
    A fisherman stood aghast,
To see the form of a maiden fair,
    Lashed close to a drifting mast.

The salt sea was frozen on her breast,
   The salt tears in her eyes;
And he saw her hair, like the brown sea-weed,
   On the billows fall and rise.

Such was the wreck of the Hesperus,
   In the midnight and the snow!
Christ save us all from a death like this,
   On the reef of Norman's Woe!

HENRY WADSWORTH LONGFELLOW

'With Ships the sea was sprinkled far and nigh'

With Ships the sea was sprinkled far and nigh,
Like stars in heaven, and joyously it showed;
Some lying fast at anchor in the road,
Some veering up and down, one knew not why.
A goodly Vessel did I then espy
Come like a giant from a haven broad;
And lustily along the bay she strode,
Her tackling rich, and of apparel high.
This Ship was naught to me, nor I to her,
Yet I pursued her with a Lover's look;
This Ship to all the rest did I prefer:
When will she turn, and whither? She will brook
No tarrying; where She comes the winds must stir:
On went She, and due north her journey took.

WILLIAM WORDSWORTH

Kelp

There is one marine production, which from its importance is worthy of a particular history. It is the kelp or *Fucus giganteus* of Solander. This plant grows on every rock from low-water mark to a great depth, both on the outer coast and within the channels. I believe, during the voyages of the *Adventure* and *Beagle*, not one rock near the surface was discovered, which was not buoyed by this floating weed. The good service it thus affords to vessels navigating near this stormy land is evident; and it certainly has saved many a one from being wrecked. I knew few things more surprising than to see this plant growing and flourishing amidst those great breakers of the western ocean, which no mass of rock, let it be ever so hard, can long resist. The stem is round, slimy, and smooth, and seldom has a diameter of so much as an inch. A few taken together are sufficiently strong to support the weight of the large loose stones to which in the inland channels they grow attached; and some of these stones are so heavy, that when drawn to the surface they can scarcely be lifted into a boat by one person.

Captain Cook, in his second voyage, says, that at Kerguelen Land 'some of this weed is of a most enormous length, though the stem is not much thicker than a man's thumb. I have mentioned, that on some of the shoals upon which it grows, we did not strike ground with a line of 24 fathoms. The depth of water, therefore, must have been greater. And as this weed does not grow in a perpendicular direction, but makes a very acute angle with the bottom, and much of it afterwards spreads many fathoms on the surface of the sea, I am well warranted to say that some of it grows to the length of sixty fathoms and upwards.' Certainly at the Falkland Islands, and about Tierra del Fuego, extensive beds frequently spring up from 10- and 15-fathom water. I do not suppose the stem of any other plant attains so great a length as 360 feet, as stated by Captain Cook. Its geographical range is very considerable; it is found from the extreme southern islets near Cape Horn, as far north, on the eastern coast (according to information given me by Mr Stokes), as lat. 43° – and on the western it was tolerably abundant, but far from luxuriant, at Chiloe, in lat. 42°. It may possibly extend a little further northward, but is soon succeeded by a different species. We thus have a range of 15° in latitude; and as Cook, who must have been well acquainted with the species, found it at Kerguelen Land, no less than 140° in longitude.

The number of living creatures of all orders, whose existence intimately depends on the kelp, is wonderful. A great volume might be written, describing the inhabitants of one of these beds of sea-weed. Almost every leaf, excepting those that float on the surface, is so thickly incrusted with coral-lines, as to be of a white colour. We find exquisitely-delicate structures, some inhabited by simple hydra-like polypi, others by more organized kinds, and beautiful compound Ascidiæ. On the flat surfaces of the leaves various patelliform shells, Trochi, uncovered molluscs, and some bivalves are attached. Innumerable crustacea frequent every part of the plant. On shaking the great entangled roots, a pile of small fish, shells, cuttle-fish, crabs of all orders, sea-eggs, star-fish, beautiful Holuthuriæ (some taking the external form of the nudibranch molluscs), Planariæ, and crawling nereidous animals of a multitude of forms, all fall out together. Often as I recurred to a branch of the kelp, I never failed to discover animals of new and curious structures. In Chiloe, where, as I have said, the kelp did not thrive very well, the numerous shells, corallines, and crustacea were absent; but there yet remained a few of the flustraceæ, and some compound Ascidiæ; the latter, however, were of different species from those in Tierra del Fuego. We here see the fucus possessing a wider range than the animals which use it as an abode.

I can only compare these great aquatic forests of the southern hemisphere with the terrestrial ones in the intertropical regions. Yet if the latter should be destroyed in any country, I do not believe nearly so many species of animals would perish, as, under similar circumstances, would happen with the kelp. Amidst the leaves of this plant numerous species of fish live, which nowhere else would find food or shelter; with their destruction the many cormorants, divers, and other fishing birds, the otters, seals, and porpoises, would soon perish also; and lastly, the Fuegian savage, the miserable lord of this miserable land, would redouble his cannibal feast, decrease in numbers, and perhaps cease to exist.

CHARLES DARWIN
from *Voyage of the* Beagle

A North Sea Storm

It was a murky confusion – here and there blotted with a color like the color of the smoke from damp fuel – of flying clouds, tossed up into most remarkable heaps, suggesting greater heights in the clouds than there were depths below them to the bottom of the deepest hollows in the earth, through which the wild moon seemed to plunge headlong, as if, in a dread disturbance of the laws of nature, she had lost her way and were frightened. There had been a wind all day; and it was rising then, with an extraordinary great sound. In another hour it had much increased, and the sky was more overcast, and it blew hard.

But, as the night advanced, the clouds closing in and densely over-spreading the whole sky, then very dark, it came on to blow, harder and harder. It still increased, until our horses could scarcely face the wind. Many times, in the dark part of the night (it was then late in September, when the nights were not short), the leaders turned about, or came to a dead stop; and we were often in serious apprehension that the coach would be blown over. Sweeping gusts of rain came up before this storm, like showers of steel; and, at those times, when there was any shelter of trees or lee walls to be got, we were fain to stop, in a sheer impossibility of continuing the struggle.

When the day broke, it blew harder and harder. I had been in Yarmouth when the seamen said it blew great guns, but I had never known the like of this, or anything approaching to it. We came to Ipswich – very late, having had to fight every inch of ground since we were ten miles out of London; and found a cluster of people in the market-place, who had risen from their beds in the night, fearful of falling chimneys. Some of these, congregating about the inn-yard while we changed horses, told us of great sheets of lead having been ripped off a high church-tower, and flung into a bye-street, which they then blocked up. Others had to tell of country people, coming in from neighbouring villages, who had seen great trees lying torn out of the earth, and whole ricks scattered about the roads and fields. Still, there was no abatement in the storm, but it blew harder.

As we struggled on, nearer and nearer to the sea, from which this mighty wind was blowing dead on shore, its force became more and more terrific. Long before we saw the sea, its spray was on our lips, and showered salt rain upon us. The water was out, over miles and miles of the flat country adjacent to Yarmouth; and every sheet and puddle lashed its banks, and had its stress of little breakers setting heavily towards us. When we came within sight of the sea, the waves on the horizon, caught at intervals above the rolling abyss, were like glimpses of another shore with towers and buildings. When at last we got into the town, the people came out to their doors, all aslant, and with streaming hair, making a wonder of the mail that had come through such a night.

I put up at the old inn, and went down to look at the sea; staggering along the street, which was strewn with sand and seaweed, and with flying blotches of sea-foam; afraid of falling slates and tiles; and holding by people I met, at angry corners. Coming near the beach, I saw, not only the boatmen, but half the people of the town, lurking behind buildings; some, now and then braving the fury of the storm to look away to sea, and blown sheer out of their course in trying to get zigzag back.

Joining these groups, I found bewailing women whose husbands were away in herring or oyster boats, which there was too much reason to think might have foundered before they could run in anywhere for safety. Grizzled old sailors were among the people, shaking their heads, as they looked from water to sky, and muttering to one another; ship-owners, excited and uneasy; children, huddling together, and peering into older faces; even stout mariners, disturbed and anxious, levelling their glasses at the sea from behind places of shelter, as if they were surveying an enemy.

The tremendous sea itself, when I could find sufficient pause to look at it, in the agitation of the blinding wind, the flying stones and sand, and the awful noise, confounded me. As the high watery walls came rolling in, and, at their highest, tumbled into surf, they looked as if the least would engulf the town. As the receding wave swept back with a hoarse roar, it seemed to scoop out deep caves in the beach, as if its purpose were to undermine the earth. When some white-headed billows thundered on, and dashed themselves to pieces before they reached the land, every fragment of the late whole seemed possessed by the full might of its wrath, rushing to be gathered to the composition of another monster. Undulating hills were changed to valleys, undulating valleys (with a solitary storm-bird sometimes skimming through them) were lifted up to hills; masses of water shivered and shook the beach with a booming sound; every shape tumultuously rolled on, as soon as made, to change its shape and place, and beat another shape and place away; the ideal shore on the horizon, with its towers and buildings, rose and fell; the clouds flew fast and thick; I seemed to see a rending and upheaving of all nature.

Not finding Ham among the people whom this memorable wind – for it is still remembered down there, as the greatest ever known to blow upon that coast – had brought together, I made my way to his house. It was shut; and as no one answered to my knocking, I went, by back ways and bye-lanes, to the yard where he worked. I learned, there, that he had gone to Lowestoft, to meet some sudden exigency of ship-repairing in which his skill was required; but that he would be back to-morrow morning, in good time.

I went back to the inn; and when I had washed and dressed, and tried to sleep, but in vain, it was five o'clock in the afternoon. I had not sat five minutes by the coffee-room fire, when the waiter, coming to stir it, as an excuse for talking, told me that two colliers had gone down, with all hands, a few miles away; and that some other ships had been seen laboring hard in the Roads, and trying, in great distress, to keep off-shore. Mercy on them, and on all poor sailors, said he, if we had another night like the last!

I was very much depressed in spirits; very solitary; and felt an uneasiness in Ham's not being there, disproportionate to the occasion. I was seriously affected, without knowing how much, by late events; and my long exposure to the fierce wind had confused me. There was that jumble in my thoughts and recollections, that I had lost the clear arrangement of time and distance. Thus, if I had gone out into the town, I should not have been surprised, I think, to encounter some one who I knew must be then in London. So to speak, there was in these respects a curious inattention in my mind. Yet it was busy, too, with all the remembrances the place naturally awakened; and they were particularly distinct and vivid.

In this state, the waiter's dismal intelligence about the ships immediately connected itself, without any effort of my volition, with my uneasiness about Ham. I was persuaded that I had an apprehension of his returning from Lowestoft by sea, and being lost. This grew so strong with me, that I resolved to go back to the yard before I took my dinner, and ask the boat-builder if he thought his attempting to return by sea at all likely? If he gave me the least reason to think so, I would go over to Lowestoft and prevent it by bringing him with me.

I hastily ordered my dinner, and went back to the yard. I was none too soon; for the boat-builder, with a lantern in his hand, was locking the yard-gate. He quite laughed, when I asked him the question, and said there was no fear; no man in his senses, or out of them, would put off in such a gale of wind, least of all Ham Peggotty, who had been born to seafaring.

So sensible of this, beforehand, that I had really felt ashamed of doing what I was nevertheless impelled to do, I went back to the inn. If such a wind could rise, I think it was rising. The howl and roar, the rattling of the doors and windows, the rumbling in the chimneys, the apparent rocking of the very house that sheltered me, and the prodigious tumult of the sea, were more fearful than in the morning. But there was now a great darkness besides; and that invested the storm with new terrors, real and fanciful.

I could not eat, I could not sit still, I could not continue stedfast to anything. Something within me, faintly answering to the storm without, tossed up the depths of my memory, and made a tumult in them. Yet, in all the hurry of my thoughts, wild running with the thundering sea, – the storm, and my uneasiness regarding Ham, were always in the foreground.

My dinner went away almost untasted, and I tried to refresh myself with a glass or two of wine. In vain. I fell into a dull slumber before the fire, without losing my consciousness, either of the uproar out of doors, or of the place in which I was. Both became overshadowed by a new and indefinable horror; and when I awoke – or rather when I shook off the lethargy that bound me in my chair – my whole frame thrilled with objectless and unintelligible fear.

I walked to and fro, tried to read an old gazetteer, listened to the awful noises: looked at faces, scenes, and figures in the fire. At length, the steady ticking of the undisturbed clock on the wall, tormented me to that degree that I resolved to go to bed.

It was reassuring, on such a night, to be told that some of the inn-servants had agreed together to sit up until morning. I went to bed, exceedingly weary and heavy; but, on my lying down, all such sensations vanished, as if by magic, and I was broad awake, with every sense refined.

For hours I lay there, listening to the wind and water; imagining, now, that I heard shrieks out at sea; now, that I distinctly heard the firing of signal guns; and now, the fall of houses in the town. I got up, several times, and looked out; but could see nothing, except the reflection in the window-panes of the faint candle I had left burning, and of my own haggard face looking in at me from the black void.

CHARLES DICKENS
from *David Copperfield*

The West African Coast

'I left in a French steamer, and she called in every blamed port they have out there, for, as far as I could see, the sole purpose of landing soldiers and custom-house officers. I watched the coast. Watching a coast as it slips by the ship is like thinking about an enigma. There it is before you – smiling, frowning, inviting, grand, mean, insipid, or savage, and always mute with an air of whispering, Come and find out. This one was almost featureless, as if still in the making, with an aspect of monotonous grimness. The edge of a colossal jungle, so dark-green as to be almost black, fringed with white surf, ran straight, like a ruled

line, far, far away along a blue sea whose glitter was blurred by
a creeping mist. The sun was fierce, the land seemed to glisten
and drip with steam. Here and there greyish-whitish specks
showed up, clustered inside the white surf, with a flag flying
above them perhaps – settlements some centuries old, and still
no bigger than pin-heads on the untouched expanse of their
background. We pounded along, stopped, landed soldiers; went
on, landed custom-house clerks to levy toll in what looked like
a God-forsaken wilderness, with a tin shed and a flag-pole lost
in it; landed more soldiers – to take care of the custom-house
clerks, presumably. Some, I heard, got drowned in the surf; but
whether they did or not, nobody seemed particularly to care.
They were just flung out there, and on we went. Every day the
coast looked the same, as though we had not moved; but we
passed various places – trading places – with names like Gran'
Bassam, Little Popo, names that seemed to belong to some
sordid farce acted in front of a sinister backcloth. The idleness
of a passenger, my isolation amongst all these men with whom
I had no point of contact, the oily and languid sea, the uniform
sombreness of the coast, seemed to keep me away from the
truth of things, within the toil of a mournful and senseless
delusion. The voice of the surf heard now and then was a positive
pleasure, like the speech of a brother. It was something natural,
that had its reason, that had a meaning. Now and then a boat
from the shore gave one a momentary contact with reality. It
was paddled by black fellows. You could see from afar the white
of their eyeballs glistening. They shouted, sang; their bodies
streamed with perspiration; they had faces like grotesque masks
– these chaps; but they had bone, muscle, a wild vitality, an
intense energy of movement, that was as natural and true as
the surf along their coast. They wanted no excuse for being
there. They were a great comfort to look at. For a time I would
feel I belonged still to a world of straightforward facts; but the
feeling would not last long. Something would turn up to scare

it away. Once, I remember, we came upon a man-of-war anchored off the coast. There wasn't even a shed there, and she was shelling the bush. It appears the French had one of their wars going on thereabouts. Her ensign dropped limp like a rag; the muzzles of the long eight-inch guns stuck out all over the low hull; the greasy, slimy swell swung her up lazily and let her down, swaying her thin masts. In the empty immensity of earth, sky, and water, there she was, incomprehensible, firing into a continent. Pop, would go one of the eight-inch guns; a small flame would dart and vanish, a little white smoke would disappear, a tiny projectile would give a feeble screech – and nothing happened. Nothing could happen. There was a touch of insanity in the proceeding, a sense of lugubrious drollery in the sight; and it was not dissipated by somebody on board assuring me earnestly there was a camp of natives – he called them enemies! – hidden out of sight somewhere.

'We gave her her letters (I heard the men in that lonely ship were dying of fever at the rate of three a-day) and went on. We called at some more places with farcical names, where the merry dance of death and trade goes on in a still and earthy atmosphere as of an overheated catacomb; all along the formless coast bordered by dangerous surf, as if Nature herself had tried to ward off intruders; in and out of rivers, streams of death in life, whose banks were rotting into mud, whose waters, thickened into slime, invaded the contorted mangroves, that seemed to writhe at us in the extremity of an impotent despair. Nowhere did we stop long enough to get a particularised impression, but the general sense of vague and oppressive wonder grew upon me. It was like a weary pilgrimage amongst hints for nightmares.'

JOSEPH CONRAD
from *Heart of Darkness*

Taken into Slavery

The first object which saluted my eyes when I arrived on the coast was the sea, and a slave-ship, which was then riding at anchor, and waiting for its cargo. These filled me with astonishment, which was soon converted into terror, which I am yet at a loss to describe, nor the then feelings of my mind. When I was carried on board I was immediately handled, and tossed up, to see if I were sound, by some of the crew; and I was now persuaded that I had gotten into a world of bad spirits, and that they were going to kill me. Their complexions too differing so much from ours, their long hair, and the language they spoke, which was very different from any I had ever heard, united to confirm me in this belief. Indeed, such were the horrors of my views and fears at the moment, that, if ten thousand worlds had been my own, I would have freely parted with them all to have exchanged my condition with that of the meanest slave in my own country. When I looked round the ship too, and saw a large furnace of copper boiling, and a multitude of black people of every description chained together, every one of their countenances expressing dejection and sorrow, I no longer doubted of my fate, and, quite overpowered with horror and anguish, I fell motionless on the deck and fainted. When I recovered a little, I found some black people about me, who I believed were some of those who brought me on board, and had been receiving their pay; they talked to me in order to cheer me, but all in vain. I asked them if we were not to be eaten by those white men with horrible looks, red faces, and long hair? They told me I was not; and one of the crew brought me a small portion of spirituous liquor in a wine glass; but, being afraid of him, I would not take it out of his hand. One of the blacks therefore took it from him and gave it to me, and I took a little down my palate, which, instead of reviving me, as they thought it would, threw me into the greatest consternation at the strange feeling it produced, having never tasted any such liquor before. Soon after this, the blacks who brought me on board went off, and left me abandoned to despair. I now saw myself deprived of all chance of returning to my native country, or even the least glimpse of hope of gaining the shore, which I now considered as friendly: and I even wished for my former slavery in preference to my present situation, which was filled with horrors of every kind, still heightened by my ignorance of what I was to undergo. I was not long suffered to indulge my grief; I was soon put down under the decks, and there I received such a salutation in my nostrils as I had never experienced in my life; so that with the loathsomeness of the stench, and crying together, I became so sick and low that I was not able to eat, nor had I the least desire to taste any thing. I now wished for the last friend, Death, to relieve me; but soon, to my grief, two of the white men offered me eatables; and, on my refusing to eat, one of them held me fast by the hands, and laid me across, I think, the windlass, and tied my feet, while the other flogged me severely. I had never experienced any thing of this kind before; and although, not being used to the water, I naturally feared that element the first time I saw it; yet, nevertheless, could I have got over the nettings, I would have jumped over the side, but I could not; and, besides, the crew used to watch us very closely who were not chained down to the decks, lest we should leap into the water; and I have seen some of these poor African prisoners most severely cut for attempting to do so, and hourly whipped for not eating. This indeed was often the case with myself. In a little time after, amongst the poor chained men, I found some of my own nation, which in a small degree gave ease to my mind. I inquired of these what was to be done with us? they gave me to understand we were to be carried to these white people's country to work for them. I then was a little revived, and thought, if it were no worse than working, my

situation was not so desperate: but still I feared I should be put
to death, the white people looked and acted, as I thought, in so
savage a manner; for I had never seen among any people such
instances of brutal cruelty; and this not only shewn towards us
blacks, but also to some of the whites themselves. One white
man in particular I saw, when we were permitted to be on deck,
flogged so unmercifully with a large rope near the foremast,
that he died in consequence of it; and they tossed him over the
side as they would have done a brute. This made me fear these
people the more; and I expected nothing less than to be treated
in the same manner. I could not help expressing my fears and
apprehensions to some of my countrymen: I asked them if these
people had no country, but lived in this hollow place the ship?
they told me they did not, but came from a distant one. 'Then,'
said I, 'how comes it in all our country we never heard of them?'
They told me, because they lived so very far off. I then asked
where were their women? had they any like themselves! I was
told they had: 'And why,' said I, 'do we not see them?' they
answered, because they were left behind. I asked how the vessel
could go? they told me they could not tell; but that there were
cloths put upon the masts by the help of the ropes I saw, and
then the vessel went on; and the white men had some spell or
magic they put in the water when they liked in order to stop
the vessel. I was exceedingly amazed at this account, and really
thought they were spirits. I therefore wished much to be from
amongst them, for I expected they would sacrifice me: but my
wishes were vain; for we were so quartered that it was impossible
for any of us to make our escape. While we staid on the coast
I was mostly on deck; and one day, to my great astonishment,
I saw one of these vessels coming in with the sails up. As soon
as the whites saw it, they gave a great shout, at which we were
amazed; and the more so as the vessel appeared larger by
approaching nearer. At last she came to an anchor in my sight,
and when the anchor was let go, I and my countrymen who

saw it were lost in astonishment to observe the vessel stop; and were now convinced it was done by magic. Soon after this the other ship got her boats out, and they came on board of us, and the people of both ships seemed very glad to see each other. Several of the strangers also shook hands with us black people, and made motions with their hands, signifying, I suppose, we were to go to their country; but we did not understand them. At last, when the ship we were in had got in all her cargo, they made ready with many fearful noises, and we were all put under deck . . .

OLAUDAH EQUIANO
from *The Interesting Narrative*

Seaward

I

The green grows ever greyer as we pass;
    The lean soil sandier; the spacious air
More breezy; raggeder the bristly grass;
    And the few crookèd leafless trees more rare.

II

And now nor grass, nor trees! But only stones
    Tufted with patches of wild rosemary
And spurge. Behind them hidden, something moans;
    And large white birds come with a questioning cry.

III

What's there, beyond? A thing unsearch'd and strange;
  Not happier, but different. Something vast
And new. Some unimaginable change
  From what has been. Perchance the end at last?

EDWARD ROBERT BULWER LYTTON

The Walrus and the
Carpenter

'The sun was shining on the sea,
    Shining with all his might:
He did his very best to make
    The billows smooth and bright –
And this was odd, because it was
    The middle of the night.

The moon was shining sulkily,
    Because she thought the sun
Had got no business to be there
    After the day was done –
"It's very rude of him," she said,
    "To come and spoil the fun!"

The sea was wet as wet could be,
    The sands were dry as dry.
You could not see a cloud, because
    No cloud was in the sky:
No birds were flying overhead –
    There were no birds to fly.

The Walrus and the Carpenter
  Were walking close at hand:
They wept like anything to see
  Such quantities of sand:
"If this were only cleared away,"
  They said, "it would be grand!"

"If seven maids with seven mops
  Swept it for half a year,
Do you suppose," the Walrus said,
  "That they could get it clear?"
"I doubt it," said the Carpenter,
  And shed a bitter tear.

"O Oysters, come and walk with us!"
  The Walrus did beseech.
"A pleasant walk, a pleasant talk,
  Along the briny beach:
We cannot do with more than four,
  To give a hand to each."

The eldest Oyster looked at him,
  But never a word he said:
The eldest Oyster winked his eye,
  And shook his heavy head —
Meaning to say he did not choose
  To leave the oyster-bed.

But four young Oysters hurried up,
  All eager for the treat:
Their coats were brushed, their faces washed,
  Their shoes were clean and neat —
And this was odd, because, you know,
  They hadn't any feet.

Four other Oysters followed them,
    And yet another four;
And thick and fast they came at last,
    And more, and more, and more –
All hopping through the frothy waves,
    And scrambling to the shore.

The Walrus and the Carpenter
    Walked on a mile or so,
And then they rested on a rock
    Conveniently low:
And all the little Oysters stood
    And waited in a row.

"The time has come," the Walrus said,
    "To talk of many things:
Of shoes – and ships – and sealing-wax –
    Of cabbages – and kings –
And why the sea is boiling hot –
    And whether pigs have wings."

"But wait a bit," the Oysters cried,
    "Before we have our chat;
For some of us are out of breath,
    And all of us are fat!"
"No hurry!" said the Carpenter.
    They thanked him much for that.

"A loaf of bread," the Walrus said,
    "Is what we chiefly need:
Pepper and vinegar besides
    Are very good indeed –
Now, if you're ready, Oysters dear,
    We can begin to feed."

"But not on us!" the Oysters cried,
  Turning a little blue.
"After such kindness, that would be
  A dismal thing to do!"
"The night is fine," the Walrus said.
  "Do you admire the view?

"It was so kind of you to come!
  And you are very nice!"
The Carpenter said nothing but
  "Cut us another slice.
I wish you were not quite so deaf –
  I've had to ask you twice!"

"It seems a shame," the Walrus said,
  "To play them such a trick.
After we've brought them out so far,
  And made them trot so quick!"
The Carpenter said nothing but
  "The butter's spread too thick!"

"I weep for you," the Walrus said:
  "I deeply sympathize."
With sobs and tears he sorted out
  Those of the largest size,
Holding his pocket-handkerchief
  Before his streaming eyes.

"O Oysters," said the Carpenter,
  "You've had a pleasant run!
Shall we be trotting home again?"
  But answer came there none –
  And this was scarcely odd, because
  They'd eaten every one.'

LEWIS CARROLL
from *Through the Looking-Glass*

'Amid this fearful trance . . .'

Amid this fearful trance, a thundering sound
He hears, and thrice the hollow decks rebound;
Upstarting from his couch on deck he sprung,
Thrice with shrill note the boatswain's whistle rung:
All hands unmoor! proclaims a boisterous cry,
All hands unmoor! the caverned rocks reply.
Roused from repose, aloft the sailors swarm,
And with their levers soon the windlass arm:
The order given, up springing with a bound,
They fix the bars, and heave the windlass round,
At every turn the clanging pauls resound:
Up-torn reluctant from its oozy cave
The ponderous anchor rises o'er the wave.
High on the slippery masts the yards ascend,
And far abroad the canvas wings extend.
Along the glassy plain the vessel glides,
While azure radiance trembles on her sides;
The lunar rays in long reflection gleam,
With silver deluging the fluid stream.
Levant and Thracian gales alternate play,
Then in th'Egyptian quarter die away.

A calm ensues; adjacent shores they dread,
The boats, with rowers manned, are sent ahead;
With cordage fastened to the lofty prow,
Aloof to sea the stately ship they tow;
The nervous crew their sweeping oars extend,
And pealing shouts the shore of Candia rend:
Success attends their skill! the danger's o'er!
The port is doubled, and beheld no more.

WILLIAM FALCONER
from *The Shipwreck*

On First Looking into
Chapman's Homer

Much have I travelled in the realms of gold,
   And many goodly states and kingdoms seen;
   Round many western islands have I been
Which bards in fealty to Apollo hold.
Oft of one wide expanse had I been told
   That deep-browed Homer ruled as his demesne;
   Yet did I never breathe its pure serene
Till I heard Chapman speak out loud and bold:
Then felt I like some watcher of the skies
   When a new planet swims into his ken;
Or like stout Cortez when with eagle eyes
   He stared at the Pacific – and all his men
Looked at each other with a wild surmise –
   Silent, upon a peak in Darien.

JOHN KEATS

The Tempest Raised by Poseidon

While this discourse emploid him. Neptune raisd
A huge, a high, and horrid sea, that seisd
Him and his ship and tost them through the Lake.
As when the violent winds together take
Heapes of drie chaffe and hurle them every way,
So his long woodstacke Neptune strooke astray.
    Then did Ulysses mount on rib, perforce,
Like to a rider of a running horse,
To stay himselfe a time, while he might shift
His drenched weeds that were Calypso's gift.
When putting strait Leucothea's Amulet
About his necke, he all his forces set
To swim, and cast him prostrate to the seas.
When powrefull Neptune saw the ruthlesse prease
Of perils siege him thus, he mov'd his head,
And this betwixt him and his heart he said:
    'So, now feele ils enow, and struggle so,
Till to your Jove-lov'd Ilanders you row.
But my mind sayes you will not so avoid
This last taske too, but be with sufferance cloid.'

GEORGE CHAPMAN

Song for All Seas, All Ships

I

To-day a rude brief recitative,
Of ships sailing the seas, each with its special flag or
    ship-signal,
Of unnamed heroes in the ships – of waves spreading and
    spreading far as the eye can reach,
Of dashing spray, and the winds piping and blowing,
And out of these a chant for the sailors of all nations,
Fitful, like a surge.

Of sea-captains young or old, and the mates, and of all
    intrepid sailors,
Of the few, very choice, taciturn, whom fate can never
    surprise nor death dismay,
Pick'd sparingly without noise by thee old ocean, chosen by
    thee,
Thou sea that pickest and cullest the race in time, and unitest
    nations,
Suckled by thee, old husky nurse, embodying thee,
Indomitable, untamed as thee.

(Ever the heroes on water or on land, by ones or twos
    appearing,
Ever the stock preserv'd and never lost, though rare, enough
    for seed preserv'd.)

II

Flaunt out O sea your separate flags of nations!
Flaunt out visible as ever the various ship-signals!
But do you reserve especially for yourself and for the soul of
    man one flag above all the rest,
A spiritual woven signal for all nations, emblem of man elate
    above death,
Token of all brave captains and all intrepid sailors and mates,
And all that went down doing their duty,
Reminiscent of them, twined from all intrepid captains young
    or old,
A pennant universal, subtly waving all time, o'er all brave
    sailors,
All seas, all ships.

WALT WHITMAN

In the Kattegat

Eleven days of weariness on board a vessel not intended for the accommodation of passengers have so exhausted my spirits, to say nothing of the other causes, with which you are already sufficiently acquainted, that it is with some difficulty I adhere to my determination of giving you my observations, as I travel through new scenes, whilst warmed with the impression they have made on me.

The captain, as I mentioned to you, promised to put me on shore at Arendal, or Gothenburg, in his way to Elsinore; but contrary winds obliged us to pass both places during the night. In the morning, however, after we had lost sight of the entrance of the latter bay, the vessel was becalmed; and the captain, to oblige me, hanging out a signal for a pilot, bore down towards the shore.

My attention was particularly directed to the light-house; and you can scarcely imagine with what anxiety I watched two long hours for a boat to emancipate me – still no one appeared. Every cloud that flitted on the horizon was hailed as a liberator, till approaching nearer, like most of the prospects sketched by hope, it dissolved under the eye into disappointment.

Weary of expectation, I then began to converse with the captain on the subject; and, from the tenor of the information my questions drew forth, I soon concluded, that, if I waited for a boat, I had little chance of getting on shore at this place. Despotism, as is usually the case, I found had here cramped the industry of man. The pilots being paid by the king, and scantily, they will not run into any danger, or even quit their hovels, if they can possibly avoid it, only to fulfil what is termed their duty. How different is it on the English coast, where, in the most stormy weather, boats immediately hail you, brought out by the expectation of extraordinary profit.

Disliking to sail for Elsinore, and still more to lie at anchor, or cruise about the coast for several days, I exerted all my rhetoric to prevail on the captain to let me have the ship's boat; and though I added the most forcible of arguments, I for a long time addressed him in vain.

It is a kind of rule at sea, not to send out a boat. The captain was a good-natured man; but men with common minds seldom break through general rules. Prudence is ever the resort of weakness; and they rarely go as far as they may in any under-taking, who are determined not to go beyond it on any account. If, however, I had some trouble with the captain, I did not lose much time with the sailors; for they, all alacrity, hoisted out the boat, the moment I obtained permission, and promised to row me to the light-house.

I did not once allow myself to doubt of obtaining a conveyance from thence round the rocks – and then away for Gothenburg – confinement is so unpleasant.

The day was fine; and I enjoyed the water till, approaching the little island, poor Marguerite, whose timidity always acts as a feeler before her adventuring spirit, began to wonder at our not seeing any inhabitants. I did not listen to her. But when, on landing, the same silence prevailed, I caught the alarm, which was not lessened by the sight of two old men, whom we forced out of their wretched hut. Scarcely human in their appearance, we with difficulty obtained an intelligible reply to our questions – the result of which was, that they had no boat, and were not allowed to quit their post, on any pretence. But, they informed us, that there was at the other side, eight or ten miles over, a pilot's dwelling; two guineas tempted the sailors to risk the captain's displeasure, and once more embark to row me over.

The weather was pleasant, and the appearance of the shore so grand, that I should have enjoyed the two hours it took to reach it, but for the fatigue which was too visible in the countenances of the sailors who, instead of uttering a complaint, were, with the thoughtless hilarity peculiar to them, joking about the possibility of the captain's taking advantage of a slight westerly breeze, which was springing up, to sail without them. Yet, in spite of their good humour, I could not help growing uneasy when the shore, receding, as it were, as we advanced, seemed to promise no end to their toil. This anxiety increased when, turning into the most picturesque bay I ever saw, my eyes sought in vain for the vestige of a human habitation. Before I could determine what step to take in such a dilemma, for I could not bear to think of returning to the ship, the sight of a barge relieved me, and we hastened towards it for information. We were immediately directed to pass some jutting rocks when we should see a pilot's hut.

There was a solemn silence in this scene, which made itself be felt. The sun-beams that played on the ocean, scarcely ruffled by the lightest breze, contrasted with the huge, dark rocks, that looked like the rude materials of creation forming the barrier of unwrought space, forcibly struck me; but I should not have been sorry if the cottage had not appeared equally tranquil. Approaching a retreat where strangers, especially women, so seldom appeared, I wondered that curiosity did not bring the beings who inhabited it to the windows or door. I did not immediately recollect that men who remain so near the brute creation, as only to exert themselves to find the food necessary to sustain life, have little or no imagination to call forth the curiosity necessary to fructify the faint glimmerings of mind which entitles them to rank as lords of the creation. – Had they either, they could not contentedly remain rooted in the clods they so indolently cultivate.

Whilst the sailors went to seek for the sluggish inhabitants, these conclusions occurred to me; and, recollecting the extreme fondness which the Parisians ever testify for novelty, their very curiosity appeared to me a proof of the progress they had made in refinement. Yes; in the art of living – in the art of escaping from the cares which embarrass the first steps towards the attainment of the pleasures of social life.

The pilots informed the sailors that they were under the direction of a lieutenant retired from the service, who spoke English; adding, that they could do nothing without his orders; and even the offer of money could hardly conquer their laziness, and prevail on them to accompany us to his dwelling. They would not go with me alone which I wanted them to have done, because I wished to dismiss the sailors as soon as possible. Once more we rowed off, they following tardily, till, turning round another bold protuberance of the rocks, we saw a boat making towards us, and soon learnt that it was the lieutenant himself, coming with some earnestness to see who we were.

To save the sailors any further toil, I had my baggage instantly removed into his boat; for, as he could speak English, a previous parley was not necessary; though Marguerite's respect for me could hardly keep her from expressing the fear, strongly marked on her countenance, which my putting ourselves into the power of a strange man excited. He pointed out his cottage; and, drawing near to it, I was not sorry to see a female figure, though I had not, like Marguerite, been thinking of robberies, murders, or the other evil which instantly, as the sailors would have said, runs foul of a woman's imagination.

MARY WOLLSTONECRAFT
from *A Short Residence in Sweden*

Biarritz

Biarritz still retained its quiddity in those days. Dusty blackberry bushes and weedy *terrains à vendre* bordered the road that led to our villa. The Carlton was still being built. Some thirty-six years had to elapse before Brigadier General Samuel McCroskey would occupy the royal suite of the Hotel du Palais, which stands on the site of a former palace, where, in the sixties, that incredibly agile medium, Daniel Home, is said to have been caught stroking with his bare foot (in imitation of a ghost hand) the kind, trustful face of Empress Eugénie. On the promenade near the Casino, an elderly flower girl, with carbon eyebrows and a painted smile, nimbly slipped the plump torus of a carnation into the buttonhole of an intercepted stroller whose left jowl accentuated its royal fold as he glanced down sideways at the coy insertion of the flower.

Along the back line of the *plage*, various seaside chairs and stools supported the parents of straw-hatted children who were playing in front on the sand. I could be seen on my knees trying to set a found comb aflame by means of a magnifying glass. Men sported white trousers that to the eye of today would look as if they had comically shrunk in the washing; ladies wore, that particular season, light coats with silk-faced lapels, hats with big crowns and wide brims, dense embroidered white veils, frill-fronted blouses, frills at their wrists, frills on their parasols. The breeze salted one's lips. At a tremendous pace a stray golden-orange butterfly came dashing across the palpitating *plage.*

Additional movement and sound were provided by vendors hawking *cacahuètes,* sugared violets, pistachio ice cream of a heavenly green, cachou pellets, and huge convex pieces of dry, gritty, waferlike stuff that came from a red barrel. With a distinctness that no later superpositions have dimmed, I see that waffleman stomp along through deep mealy sand, with the heavy cask on his bent back. When called, he would sling it off his shoulder by a twist of its strap, bang it down on the sand in a Tower of Pisa position, wipe his face with his sleeve, and proceed to manipulate a kind of arrow-and-dial arrangement with numbers on the lid of the cask. The arrow rasped and whirred around. Luck was supposed to fix the size of a sou's worth of wafer. The bigger the piece, the more I was sorry for him.

The process of bathing took place on another part of the beach. Professional bathers, burly Basques in black bathing suits, were there to help ladies and children enjoy the terrors of the surf. Such a *baigneur* would place you with your back to the incoming wave and hold you by the hand as the rising, rotating mass of foamy, green water violently descended upon you from behind, knocking you off your feet with one mighty wallop. After a dozen of these tumbles, the *baigneur,* glistening like a seal, would lead his panting, shivering, moistly snuffling charge landward, to the flat foreshore, where an unforgettable old woman with gray hairs on her chin promptly chose a bathing robe from several hanging on a clothesline. In the security of a little cabin, one would be helped by yet another attendant to peel off one's soggy, sand-heavy bathing suit. It would plop onto the boards, and, still shivering, one would step out of it and trample on its bluish, diffuse stripes. The cabin smelled of pine. The attendant, a hunchback with beaming wrinkles, brought a basin of steaming-hot water, in which one immersed one's feet. From him I learned, and have preserved ever since in a glass cell of my memory, that 'butterfly' in the Basque language is *misericolettea* – or at least it sounded so (among the seven words I have found in dictionaries the closest approach is *micheletea*).

VLADIMIR NABOKOV
from 'First Love'

Horace's Ode 1.14

Oh Ship! new billows sweep thee out
Seaward. What wilt thou? Hold the port, be stout:
    See'st not thy mast
How rent by stiff Southwestern blast?

Thy side, of rowers how forlorn?
Thine hull, with groaning yards, with rigging torn,
    Can ill sustain
The fierce, and ever fiercer main;

Thy gods, no more than sails entire,
From whom yet once thy need might aid require,
    Oh Pontic Pine,
The first of woodland stocks is thine,

Yet race and name are but as dust.
Not painted sterns give storm-tost seamen trust;
    Unless thou dare
To be the sport of storms, beware.

O fold at best a weary weight,
A yearning care and constant strain of late,
    O shun the seas
That gird those glittering Cyclades.

WILLIAM EWART GLADSTONE

An Explosion in the Hold

No one was killed, or even disabled, but everyone was more or less hurt. You should have seen them! Some were in rags, with black faces, like coalheavers, like sweeps, and had bullet heads that seemed closely cropped, but were in fact singed to the skin. Others of the watch below, awakened by being shot out from their collapsing bunks, shivered incessantly, and kept on groaning even as we went about our work. But they all worked. That crew of Liverpool hard cases had in them the right stuff. It's my experience they always have. It is the sea that gives it – the vastness, the loneliness surrounding their dark stolid souls. Ah! Well! we stumbled, we crept, we fell, we barked our shins on the wreckage, we hauled. The masts stood, but we did not know how much they might be charred down below. It was nearly calm, but a long swell ran from the west and made her roll. They might go at any moment. We looked at them with apprehension. One could not foresee which way they would fall.

Then we retreated aft and looked about us. The deck was a tangle of planks on edge, of planks on end, of splinters, of ruined woodwork. The masts rose from that chaos like big trees above a matted undergrowth. The interstices of that mass of wreckage were full of something whitish, sluggish, stirring – of something that was like a greasy fog. The smoke of the invisible fire was coming up again, was trailing, like a poisonous thick mist in some valley choked with dead wood. Already lazy wisps were beginning to curl upwards amongst the mass of splinters. Here and there a piece of timber, stuck upright, resembled a post. Half of a fife-rail had been shot through the foresail, and the sky made a patch of glorious blue in the ignobly soiled canvas. A portion of several boards holding together had fallen across the rail, and one end protruded overboard, like a gangway leading upon nothing, like a gangway leading over the deep sea, leading to death – as if inviting us to walk the plank at once and be done with our ridiculous troubles.

JOSEPH CONRAD
from *Youth*

September, 1802. Near Dover

Inland, within a hollow vale, I stood;
And saw, while sea was calm and air was clear,
The coast of France – the coast of France how near!
Drawn almost into frightful neighbourhood.
I shrunk; for verily the barrier flood
Was like a lake, or river bright and fair,
A span of waters; yet what power is there!
What mightiness for evil and for good!
Even so doth God protect us if we be
Virtuous and wise. Winds blow, and waters roll,

Strength to the brave, and Power, and Deity;
Yet in themselves are nothing! One decree
Spake laws to *them*, and said that by the soul
Only, the Nations shall be great and free.

WILLIAM WORDSWORTH

The Voyage to Boue-Marine

Black was the river as a torrent of ink: lights glanced on it from the piles of building round, ships rocked on its bosom. They rowed me up to several vessels; I read by lantern-light their names painted in great, white letters on a dark ground. 'The Ocean,' 'The Phœnix,' 'The Consort,' 'The Dolphin,' were passed in turn; but 'The Vivid' was my ship, and it seemed she lay further down.

Down the sable flood we glided; I thought of the Styx, and of Charon rowing some solitary soul to the Land of Shades. Amidst the strange scene, with a chilly wind blowing in my face, and midnight-clouds dropping rain above my head; with two rude rowers for companions, whose insane oaths still tortured my ear, I asked myself if I was wretched or terrified. I was neither. Often in my life have I been far more so under comparatively safe circumstances. 'How is this?' said I. 'Methinks I am animated and alert, instead of being depressed and apprehensive?' I could not tell how it was.

'THE VIVID' started out, white and glaring, from the black night at last. 'Here you are!' said the waterman, and instantly demanded six shillings.

'You ask too much,' I said. He drew off from the vessel and swore he would not embark me till I paid it. A young man, the steward as I found afterwards, was looking over the ship's side; he grinned a smile in anticipation of the coming contest; to disappoint him, I paid the money. Three times that afternoon I had given crowns where I should have given shillings; but I consoled myself with the reflection, 'It is the price of experience.'

'They've cheated you!' said the steward exultantly when I got on board. I answered phlegmatically that 'I knew it,' and went below.

A stout, handsome, and showy woman was in the ladies' cabin; I asked to be shown my berth; she looked hard at me, muttered something about it being unusual for passengers to come on board at that hour, and seemed disposed to be less than civil. What a face she had – so comely – so insolent and so selfish!

'Now that I am on board, I shall certainly stay here,' was my answer. 'I will trouble you to show me my berth.'

She complied, but sullenly. I took off my bonnet, arranged my things, and lay down. Some difficulties had been passed through; a sort of victory was won: my homeless, anchorless, unsupported mind had again leisure for a brief repose: till the 'Vivid' arrived in harbour, no further action would be required of me, but then . . . Oh! I could not look forward. Harassed, exhausted, I lay in a half-trance.

The stewardess talked all night; not to me, but to the young steward, her son and her very picture. He passed in and out of the cabin continually: they disputed, they quarrelled, they made it up again twenty times in the course of the night. She professed to be writing a letter home, – she said to her father; she read passages of it aloud, heeding me no more than a stock – perhaps she believed me asleep: several of these passages appeared to comprise family secrets, and bore special reference to one 'Charlotte,' a younger sister who, from the bearing of the epistle, seemed to be on the brink of perpetrating a romantic and imprudent match; loud was the protest of this elder lady against the distasteful union. The dutiful son laughed his mother's correspondence to scorn. She defended it, and raved at him.

They were a strange pair. She might be thirty-nine or forty, and was buxom and blooming as a girl of twenty. Hard, loud, vain and vulgar, her mind and body alike seemed brazen and imperishable. I should think, from her childhood, she must have lived in public stations; and in her youth might very likely have been a bar-maid.

Towards morning her discourse ran on a new theme: 'the Watsons,' a certain expected family-party of passengers, known to her, it appeared, and by her much esteemed on account of the handsome profit realized in their fees. She said, 'it was as good as a little fortune to her whenever this family crossed.'

At dawn all were astir, and by sunrise the passengers came on board. Boisterous was the welcome given by the stewardess to the 'Watsons,' and great was the bustle made in their honour. They were four in number, two males and two females. Besides them, there was but one other passenger – a young lady, whom a gentlemanly, though languid-looking man escorted. The two groups offered a marked contrast. The Watsons were doubtless rich people, for they had the confidence of conscious wealth in their bearing; the women – youthful both of them, and one perfectly handsome, as far as physical beauty went – were dressed richly, gaily, and absurdly out of character for the circumstances. Their bonnets with bright flowers, their velvet cloaks and silk dresses seemed better suited for park or promenade than for a damp packet-deck. The men were of low stature, plain, fat, and vulgar; the oldest, plainest, greasiest, broadest, I soon found was the husband – the bridegroom I suppose, for she was very young – of the beautiful girl. Deep was my amazement at this discovery; and deeper still when I perceived that, instead of being desperately wretched in such a union, she was gay even to giddiness. 'Her laughter,' I reflected, 'must be the mere frenzy of despair.' And even while this thought was crossing my mind, as I stood leaning quiet and solitary against the ship's side, she came tripping up to me, an utter stranger, with a camp stool in her hand, and smiling a smile of which the levity puzzled and startled me, though it showed a perfect set of perfect teeth, she offered me the accommodation of this piece of furniture. I declined it, of course with all the courtesy I could put into my manner; she danced off heedless and lightsome. She must have been good-natured; but what had made her marry that individual, who was at least as much like an oil-barrel as a man?

The other lady-passenger, with the gentleman-companion, was quite a girl, pretty and fair; her simple print dress, untrimmed straw-bonnet, and large shawl, gracefully worn, formed a costume plain to quakerism: yet, for her, becoming enough. Before the gentleman quitted her, I observed him throwing a glance of scrutiny over all the passengers, as if to ascertain in what company his charge would be left. With a most dissatisfied air did his eye turn from the ladies with the gay flowers: he looked at me, and then he spoke to his daughter, niece, or whatever she was; she also glanced in my direction, and slightly curled her short, pretty lip. It might be myself, or it might be my homely mourning-habit that elicited this mark of contempt; more likely both. A bell rang; her father (I afterwards knew that it was her father) kissed her and returned to land. The packet sailed.

Foreigners say that it is only English girls who can thus be trusted to travel alone, and deep is their wonder at the daring confidence of English parents and guardians. As for the 'jeunes Miss,' by some their intrepidity is pronounced masculine and 'inconvenant,' others regard them as the passive victims of an educational and theological system which wantonly dispenses with proper 'surveillance.' Whether this particular young lady was of the sort that can the most safely be left unwatched, I do not know: or rather did not *then* know: but it soon appeared that the dignity of solitude was not to her taste. She paced the deck once or twice backwards and forwards; she looked with a little sour air of disdain at the flaunting silks and velvets, and the bears which thereon danced attendance, and eventually she approached me and spoke.

'Are you fond of a sea-voyage?' was her question.

I explained that my *fondness* for a sea-voyage had yet to undergo the test of experience: I had never made one.

'Oh how charming!' cried she. 'I quite envy you the novelty: first impressions, you know, are so pleasant. Now I have made so many, I quite forget the first: I am quite *blasée* about the sea and all that.'

I could not help smiling.

'Why do you laugh at me?' she inquired, with a frank testiness that pleased me better than her other talk.

'Because you are so young to be *blasée* about anything.'

'I am seventeen' (a little piqued).

'You hardly look sixteen. Do you like travelling alone?'

'Bah! I care nothing about it. I have crossed the Channel ten times, alone; but then I take care never to be long alone: I always make friends.'

'You will scarcely make many friends this voyage, I think' (glancing at the Watson-group, who were now laughing and making a great deal of noise on deck).

'Not of those odious men and women,' said she: 'such people should be steerage passengers. Are you going to school?'

'No.'

'Where are you going?'

'I have not the least idea – beyond, at least, the Port of Bouemarine.'

She stared, then carelessly ran on:

'I am going to school. Oh the number of foreign schools I have been at in my life! And yet I am quite an ignoramus. I know nothing – nothing in the world – I assure you; except that I play and dance beautifully, – and French and German of course I know, to speak; but I can't read or write them very well. Do you know they wanted me to translate a page of an

easy German book into English the other day, and I couldn't
do it. Papa was so mortified: he says it looks as if M. de
Bassompierre – my god-papa, who pays all my school-bills
– had thrown away all his money. And then, in matters of
information – in history, geography, arithmetic, and so on, I
am quite a baby; and I write English so badly – such spelling and
grammar, they tell me. Into the bargain I have quite forgotten my
religion; they call me a Protestant, you know, but really I am
not sure whether I am one or not: I don't well know the
difference between Romanism and Protestantism. However, I
don't in the least care for that. I was a Lutheran once at Bonn
– dear Bonn! – charming Bonn! – where there were so many
handsome students. Every nice girl in our school had an admirer;
they knew our hours for walking out, and almost always passed
us on the promenade: "Schönes Mädchen," we used to hear
them say. I was excessively happy at Bonn!'

'And where are you now?' I inquired.

'Oh! at – *chose*,' said she.

Now Miss Ginevra Fanshawe (such was this young person's
name) only substituted this word '*chose*' in temporary oblivion
of the real name. It was a habit she had: '*chose*' came in at every
turn in her conversation – the convenient substitute for any
missing word in any language she might chance at the time to
be speaking. French girls often do the like; from them she had
caught the custom. '*Chose*,' however, I found, in this instance,
stood for Villette – the great capital of the great kingdom of
Labassecour.

'Do you like Villette?' I asked.

'Pretty well. The natives, you know, are intensely stupid and
vulgar; but there are some nice English families.'

'Are you in a school?'

'Yes.'

'A good one?'

'Oh no! horrid: but I go out every Sunday, and care nothing

about the *maîtresses* or the *professeurs*, or the *élèves*, and send
lessons *au diable*; (one daren't say that in English, you know,
but it sounds quite right in French,) and thus I get on charmingly
. . . You are laughing at me again?'

'No – I am only smiling at my own thoughts.'

'What are they?' (without waiting for an answer) – 'Now *do*
tell me where you are going.'

'Where Fate may lead me. My business is to earn a living
where I can find it.'

'To earn!' (in consternation) 'are you poor then?'

'As poor as Job.'

(After a pause) 'Bah! how unpleasant! But *I* know what it is
to be poor: they are poor enough at home – papa and mama,
and all of them. Papa is called Captain Fanshawe; he is an officer
on half-pay, but well-descended, and some of our connections
are great enough; but my uncle and god-papa de Bassompierre,
who lives in France, is the only one that helps us: he educates
us girls. I have five sisters and three brothers. By-and-by we are
to marry – rather elderly gentlemen, I suppose, with cash: papa
and mama manage that. My sister Augusta is married now to
a man much older-looking than papa. Augusta is very beautiful
– not in my style – but dark; her husband, Mr Davies, had the
yellow fever in India, and he is still the colour of a guinea; but
then he is rich, and Augusta has her carriage and establishment,
and we all think she has done perfectly well. Now this is better
than "earning a living," as you say. By the way, are you clever?'

'No – not at all.'

'You can play, sing, speak three or four languages?'

'By no means.'

'Still I think you are clever' (a pause and a yawn). 'Shall you
be sea-sick?'

'Shall you?'

'Oh, immensely! as soon as ever we get in sight of the sea: I
begin, indeed, to feel it already. I shall go below; and won't I

order about that fat, odious stewardess. Heureusement je sais faire aller mon monde.' Down she went.

It was not long before the other passengers followed her: throughout the afternoon I remained on deck alone. When I recall the tranquil, and even happy mood in which I passed those hours, and remember, at the same time, the position in which I was placed: its hazardous – some would have said its hopeless – character; I feel that, as –

> Stone walls do not a prison make,
> Nor iron bars – a cage.

so peril, loneliness, an uncertain future, are not oppressive evils, so long as the frame is healthy and the faculties are employed; so long, especially, as Liberty lends us her wings, and Hope guides us by her star.

I was not sick till long after we passed Margate, and deep was the pleasure I drank in with the sea-breeze; divine the delight I drew from the heaving channel-waves, from the seabirds on their ridges, from the white sails on their dark distance, from the quiet, yet beclouded sky, overhanging all. In my reverie, methought I saw the continent of Europe, like a wide dream-land, far away. Sunshine lay on it, making the long coast one line of gold; tiniest tracery of clustered town and snow-gleaming tower, of woods deep-massed, of heights serrated, of smooth pasturage and veiny stream, embossed the metal-bright prospect. For background, spread a sky, solemn and dark-blue, and – grand with imperial promise, soft with tints of enchantment – strode from north to south a God-bent bow, an arch of hope.

Cancel the whole of that, if you please, reader – or rather let it stand, and draw thence a moral – an alternative, text-hand copy –

> Day-dreams are delusions of the demon.

Becoming excessively sick, I faltered down into the cabin.

Miss Fanshawe's berth chanced to be next mine; and, I am sorry to say, she tormented me with an unsparing selfishness during the whole time of our mutual distress. Nothing could exceed her impatience and fretfulness. The Watsons, who were very sick too, and on whom the stewardess attended with shameless partiality, were stoics compared with her. Many a time since have I noticed, in persons of Ginevra Fanshawe's light, careless temperament, and fair, fragile style of beauty, an entire incapacity to endure: they seem to sour in adversity, like small-beer in thunder: the man who takes such a woman for his wife, ought to be prepared to guarantee her an existence all sunshine. Indignant at last with her teazing peevishness, I curtly requested her 'to hold her tongue.' The rebuff did her good, and it was observable that she liked me no worse for it.

As dark night drew on, the sea roughened: larger waves swayed strong against the vessel's side. It was strange to reflect that blackness and water were round us, and to feel the ship ploughing straight on her pathless way, despite noise, billow, and rising gale. Articles of furniture began to fall about, and it became needful to lash them to their places; the passengers grew sicker than ever; Miss Fanshawe declared, with groans, that she must die.

'Not just yet, honey,' said the stewardess. 'We're just in port.' Accordingly, in another quarter of an hour, a calm fell upon us all; and about midnight the voyage ended.

I was sorry: yes, I was sorry. My resting-time was past; my difficulties – my stringent difficulties – recommenced. When I went on deck, the cold air and black scowl of the night seemed to rebuke me for my presumption in being where I was: the lights of the foreign sea-port town, glimmering round the foreign harbour, met me like unnumbered threatening eyes.

CHARLOTTE BRONTË
from *Villette*

Beeny Cliff

I

O the opal and the sapphire of that wandering western sea,
And the woman riding high above with bright hair flapping
    free –
The woman whom I loved so, and who loyally loved me.

II

The pale mews plained below us, and the waves seemed far
    away
In a nether sky, engrossed in saying their ceaseless babbling
    say,
As we laughed light-heartedly aloft on that clear-sunned
    March day.

III

A little cloud then cloaked us, and there flew an irised rain,
And the Atlantic dyed its levels with a dull misfeatured stain,
And then the sun burst out again, and purples prinked the
    main.

IV

– Still in all its chasmal beauty bulks old Beeny to the sky,
And shall she and I not go there once again now March is
    nigh,
And the sweet things said in that March say anew there by
    and by?

V

What if still in chasmal beauty looms that wild weird western
    shore,
The woman now is – elsewhere – whom the ambling pony
    bore,
And nor knows nor cares for Beeny, and will laugh there
    nevermore.

THOMAS HARDY

By the Seashore

Upon the reedy margin of the shore,
    Shallow and waste, I stand,
And hear far Ocean's low continuous roar
    Over the flats and sand.

The wide gray sky hangs low above the verge,
    No white-winged sea-bird flies;
No sound, save the eternal-sounding surge,
    With equal fall and rise.

While the salt sea-wind whispers in my ears,
    Fitful and desolate,
I seem absolved from the departed years,
    Not grieved and not elate.

WILLIAM CALDWELL ROSCOE

The Pococks' Picnic

The day after St Agatha's broke up for the summer holidays came the Pococks' picnic, for Olive's birthday. The place was Wanchurch, known for immense sands which stretch out to and along the sea from under the grass-topped sea wall defending the Marsh. The Pococks were thought highly of for this choice by all children asked. By now, halfway through the long summer, everybody was sated with pebbly beaches. Out there at Wanchurch, with its ghostly name, grew sea-pinks and even yellow sea-poppies. And the place was your own. Its great distance away to the west of Southstone, twelve miles, made to be going there a great outing. The thoughtful Pococks had overcome what could have been a problem for some guests by chartering a small motor chara-banc – open, but having a canvas hood able to be erected in case of rain. The July weather had been causing some though no great anxiety. To be on the safe side, children were asked to bring mackintoshes, on the understanding that their having done so would make it still more improbable that they would need them. Also, own rugs for sitting on. Of all things else, the Pococks took charge.

'The Pococks' picnic.' 'The Pococks' picnic.' The sound had the spell of alliteration. Or incantation, chanted round and around IVa classroom while school days ran out and the weather played cat-and-mouse. Every girl in IVa had been asked, of course.

Not all the party came in the charabanc. Two or three families from the Marsh, known to the Pococks who had a wide acquaintanceship, came over on bicycles or in pony traps. The Pococks, with the exception of Olive (who made a queenly journey amid her schoolfellows), came in their large motor car, bringing hampers, napkin-covered baskets, cake-boxes, string bags stretched to bursting-point, and so on. Aubrey Artworth borrowed Cuth's motor bike and deposited Sheikie – only, then, to tear away somewhere else. Mrs Piggott, one of the few mothers to be invited, was gladly an occupant of the charabanc. To keep the picnic within manageable size, it had been decided to cut down on parents as far as possible. Mothers here today were old Pocock family friends – not so Mrs Piggott, who had been asked because Mrs Pocock often thought she looked sad. 'I often wish,' Mrs Pocock had often said, 'one could know her better.' Here was an opportunity.

There were three or four popular fathers, and one uncle, vouched for by his owner as being funny. All were civilians. Clare Burkin-Jones's father's joining the party was, alas, known to be unlikely. 'Not much hope, I don't honestly think, Mrs Pocock,' his sombre child said. As for little boys, they were not in the majority. Most of them were girls' brothers. There was a small, not highly esteemed representation from St Swithin's. Trevor Artworth, met by Olive with Sheila, had chivalrously been invited by Olive; brushed off the Cuth motor bike by his elder brother, who'd asked him if he imagined this was a bus, he had to make a rush for the charabanc, into which he'd succeeded in squeezing himself at the last moment.

Motor conveyances drew up, there to wait for the rest of the afternoon, on the landward side of the sea wall. When the charabanc came to port, the Pococks, like noble humanized ants, still were staggering to and fro with hampers. The children out of the charabanc cataracted down off the wall at another point, shouting – at the foot, however, they fell silent, looking around them, calculatingly, at the large species. Mrs Piggott, wearing the tussore dustcoat and with her hat bound on with a chiffon motor-veil, scrambled up the land side of the sea wall among the children, on the heels of her daughter. When she reached the top, wind caught the transparent mauve ends of the veil, sending them flying against the sky – which was so lightly grey as to itself seem a veil over wide light. There she stood a minute, looking down at the sands, smiling at the beginnings of so much pleasure: a weather-signal.

ELIZABETH BOWEN

from *The Little Girls*

The Light-Keeper

I

The brilliant kernel of the night,
The flaming lightroom circles me:
I sit within a blaze of light
Held high above the dusky sea.
Far off the surf doth break and roar
Along bleak miles of moonlit shore,
Where through the tides the tumbling wave
Falls in an avalanche of foam
And drives its churnèd waters home
Up many an undercliff and cave.

The clear bell chimes: the clockworks strain:
The turning lenses flash and pass,
Frame turning within glittering frame
With frosty gleam of moving glass:
Unseen by me, each dusky hour
The sea-waves welter up the tower
Or in the ebb subside again;
And ever and anon all night,
Drawn from afar by charm of light,
A sea-bird beats against the pane.

And lastly when dawn ends the night
And belts the semi-orb of sea,
The tall, pale pharos in the light
Looks white and spectral as may be.
The early ebb is out: the green
Straight belt of seaweed now is seen,
That round the basement of the tower
Marks out the interspace of tide;
And watching men are heavy-eyed,
And sleepless lips are dry and sour.

The night is over like a dream:
The sea-birds cry and dip themselves;
And in the early sunlight, steam
The newly-bared and dripping shelves,
Around whose verge the glassy wave
With lisping wash is heard to lave;
While, on the white tower lifted high,
With yellow light in faded glass
The circling lenses flash and pass
And sickly shine against the sky.

II

As the steady lenses circle
With a frosty gleam of glass;
And the clear bell chimes,
And the oil brims over the lip of the burner,
Quiet and still at his desk,
The lonely Light-Keeper
Holds his vigil.

Lured from afar,
The bewildered seagull beats
Dully against the lantern;
Yet he stirs not, lifts not his head
From the desk where he reads,
Lifts not his eyes to see
The chill blind circle of night
Watching him through the panes.
This is his country's guardian,
The outmost sentry of peace.
This is the man,
Who gives up all that is lovely in living
For the means to live.

Poetry cunningly gilds
The life of the Light-Keeper,
Held on high in the blackness
In the burning kernel of night:
The seaman sees and blesses him;
The Poet, deep in a sonnet,
Numbers his inky fingers
Fitly to praise him;
Only we behold him,
Sitting, patient and stolid,
Martyr to a salary.

ROBERT LOUIS STEVENSON

The Enviable Isles

Through storms you reach them and from storms are free.
  Afar described, the foremost drear in hue,
But, nearer, green; and, on the marge, the sea
  Makes thunder low and mist of rainbowed dew.

But, inland, where the sleep that folds the hills
A dreamier sleep, the trance of God, instills –
  On uplands hazed, in wandering airs aswoon,
Slow-swaying palms salute love's cypress tree
  Adown in vale where pebbly runlets croon
A song to lull all sorrow and all glee.

Sweet-fern and moss in many a glade are here,
  Where, strown in flocks, what cheek-flushed myriads lie
Dimpling in dream – unconscious slumberers mere,
  While billows endless round the beaches die.

HERMAN MELVILLE

from *Psalm 107*

Such as in ships and brittle barks into the seas descend,
Their merchandise through fearful floods to compass and to
    end;
Those men are forced to behold the Lord's works what they
    be,
And in the dangerous deep, the same most marvellous they
    see.

For at his word the stormy wind ariseth in a rage,
And stirreth up the surges so as naught can them assuage.
Then are they lifted up so high the clouds they seem to gain,
And plunging down the depth until their souls consume with
    pain.

And like a drunkard, to and fro now here now there they reel,
As men with fear of wit bereft or had of sense no feel.
Then did they cry in their distress unto the Lord for aid;
Who did remove their troublous state, according as they
    pray'd.

For with his word the Lord doth make the sturdy storms to
    cease;
So that the great waves from their rage are brought to rest
    and peace.
Then are men glad when rest is come which they so much
    did crave;
And are by him in haven brought, which they so fain would
    have.

WILLIAM KETHE

from *Psalm 107*

23 They that go down to the sea in ships, that do business in
great waters;
24 These see the works of the LORD, and his wonders in the
deep.
25 For he commandeth, and raiseth the stormy wind, which
lifteth up the waves thereof.
26 They mount up to the heaven, they go down again to the
depths: their soul is melted because of trouble.

27 They reel to and fro, and stagger like a drunken man, and are at their wit's end.

28 Then they cry unto the LORD in their trouble, and he bringeth them out of their distresses.

29 He maketh the storm a calm, so that the waves thereof are still.

30 Then are they glad because they be quiet; so he bringeth them unto their desired haven.

AUTHORIZED VERSION

A Wreck off the Isle of Man

As the breeze then blew, they were soon abreast of the westward headland, bounding the bay of Poolvash; and the question was started whether they should run out to sea, or keep along the shore. The wisest proceeding, in the event of the wind failing them, was to keep by the land. Midwinter altered the course of the boat, and they sailed on smoothly in a south-westerly direction, abreast of the coast.

Little by little the cliffs rose in height, and the rocks, massed wild and jagged, showed rifted black chasms yawning deep in their seaward sides. Off the bold promontory called Spanish Head, Midwinter looked ominously at his watch. But Allan pleaded hard for half-an-hour more, and for a glance at the famous channel of the Sound, which they were now fast nearing, and of which he had heard some startling stories from the workmen employed on his yacht. The new change which Midwinter's compliance with this request rendered it necessary to make in the course of the boat, brought her close to the wind; and revealed, on one side, the grand view of the southernmost shores of the Isle of Man, and, on the other, the black precipices of the islet called the Calf, separated from the mainland by the dark and dangerous channel of the Sound.

Once more Midwinter looked at his watch. 'We have gone far enough,' he said. 'Stand by the sheet!'

'Stop!' cried Allan, from the bows of the boat. 'Good God! here's a wrecked ship right ahead of us!'

Midwinter let the boat fall off a little, and looked where the other pointed.

There, stranded midway between the rocky boundaries on either side of the Sound – there, never again to rise on the living waters from her grave on the sunken rock; lost and lonely in the quiet night; high, and dark, and ghostly in the yellow moonshine, lay the Wrecked Ship.

'I know the vessel,' said Allan, in great excitement. 'I heard my workmen talking of her yesterday. She drifted in here, on a pitch dark night, when they couldn't see the lights. A poor old worn-out merchant-man, Midwinter, that the shipbrokers have bought to break up. Let's run in, and have a look at her.'

Midwinter hesitated. All the old sympathies of his sea-life strongly inclined him to follow Allan's suggestion – but the wind was falling light; and he distrusted the broken water and the swirling currents of the channel ahead. 'This is an ugly place to take a boat into, when you know nothing about it,' he said.

'Nonsense!' returned Allan. 'It's as light as day, and we float in two feet of water.'

Before Midwinter could answer, the current caught the boat, and swept them onward through the channel, straight towards the Wreck.

'Lower the sail,' said Midwinter quietly, 'and ship the oars. We are running down on her fast enough now; whether we like it or not.'

Both well accustomed to the use of the oar, they brought the

course of the boat under sufficient control to keep her on the
smoothest side of the channel – the side which was nearest to
the Islet of the Calf. As they came swiftly up with the wreck,
Midwinter resigned his oar to Allan; and, watching his opportunity, caught a hold with the boat-hook on the forechains of the
vessel. The next moment they had the boat safely in hand, under
the lee of the Wreck.

The ship's ladder used by the workmen hung over the forechains. Mounting it, with the boat's rope in his teeth, Midwinter
secured one end, and lowered the other to Allan in the boat.
'Make that fast,' he said, 'and wait till I see if it's safe on board.'
With those words, he disappeared behind the bulwark.

'Wait?' repeated Allan, in the blankest astonishment at
his friend's excessive caution. 'What on earth does he mean?
I'll be hanged if I wait – where one of us goes, the other goes
too!'

He hitched the loose end of the rope round the forward
thwart of the boat; and, swinging himself up the ladder, stood
the next moment on the deck. 'Anything very dreadful on
board?' he inquired sarcastically, as he and his friend met.

Midwinter smiled. 'Nothing whatever,' he replied. 'But I
couldn't be sure that we were to have the whole ship to ourselves,
till I got over the bulwark, and looked about me.'

Allan took a turn on the deck, and surveyed the wreck critically
from stem to stern.

'Not much of a vessel,' he said; 'the Frenchmen generally
build better ships than this.'

Midwinter crossed the deck, and eyed Allan in a momentary
silence.

'Frenchmen?' he repeated, after an interval. 'Is this vessel
French?'

'Yes.'

'How do you know?'

'The men I have got at work on the yacht told me. They know all about her.'

Midwinter came a little nearer. His swarthy face began to look, to Allan's eyes, unaccountably pale in the moonlight.

'Did they mention what trade she was engaged in?'

'Yes. – The timber-trade.'

As Allan gave that answer, Midwinter's lean brown hand clutched him fast by the shoulder; and Midwinter's teeth chattered in his head, like the teeth of a man struck by a sudden chill.

'Did they tell you her name?' he asked, in a voice that dropped suddenly to a whisper.

'They did, I think. But it has slipped my memory. – Gently, old fellow; those long claws of yours are rather tight on my shoulder.'

'Was the name –?' he stopped; removed his hand; and dashed away the great drops that were gathering on his forehead – 'Was the name *La Grace de Dieu?*'

'How the deuce did you come to know it? That's the name, sure enough. *La Grace de Dieu.*'

At one bound, Midwinter leapt on the bulwark of the wreck.

'The boat!!!' he cried, with a scream of horror that rang far and wide through the stillness of the night, and brought Allan instantly to his side.

The lower end of the carelessly-hitched rope was loose on the water; and, a-head, in the track of the moonlight, a small black object was floating out of view. The boat was adrift.

WILKIE COLLINS
from *Armadale*

'If by your art, my dearest father . . .'

MIRANDA

If by your art, my dearest father, you have
Put the wild waters in this roar, allay them.
The sky it seems would pour down stinking pitch,
But that the sea, mounting to th'welkin's cheek,
Dashes the fire out. O, I have suffered
With those that I saw suffer! A brave vessel,
Who had, no doubt, some noble creature in her,
Dashed all to pieces. O, the cry did knock
Against my very heart! Poor souls, they perished.
Had I been any god of power, I would
Have sunk the sea within the earth, or ere
It should the good ship so have swallowed and
The fraughting souls within her.

PROSPERO   Be collected.
No more amazement. Tell your piteous heart
There's no harm done.

MIRANDA   O, woe the day!

PROSPERO   No harm.
I have done nothing but in care of thee,
Of thee, my dear one, thee my daughter, who
Art ignorant of what thou art, naught knowing
Of whence I am, nor that I am more better
Than Prospero, master of a full poor cell,
And thy no greater father.

MIRANDA   More to know
Did never meddle with my thoughts.

PROSPERO   'Tis time
I should inform thee farther. Lend thy hand,
And pluck my magic garment from me. – So,
Lie there, my art. – Wipe thou thine eyes. Have comfort.

The direful spectacle of the wrack, which touched
The very virtue of compassion in thee,
I have with such provision in mine art
So safely ordered, that there is no soul –
No, not so much perdition as an hair
Betid to any creature in the vessel
Which thou heard'st cry, which thou sawst sink. Sit down.
For thou must now know farther.

WILLIAM SHAKESPEARE
from *The Tempest*, I, 2

A Voyage to Arctic Russia

The 23rd of April, Saturday, being St Mark's Day, we departed from Blackwall. The right worshipful Sebastian Cabot came aboard our pinnace at Gravesend, with divers gentlemen and gentlewomen, the good old gentleman wishing them to pray for the good fortune, and prosperous success of the *Searchthrift*, our pinnace.

Friday the 15th of May we were within 7 leagues of the shore, on the coast of Norway: Saturday at an east sun we came to St Dunstan's Island, which island I so named.

June. We weighed in Corpus Christi Bay, at a northeast and by east sun; the bay is almost half a league deep: the headland which is Corpus Christi point, lieth one league from the head of the bay, where we had a great tide, like a race over the flood.

Thursday at six of the clock in the morning, there came aboard of us one of the Russian lodias, rowing with twenty oars. The master of the boat presented me with a great loaf of bread, four dried pikes, and a peck of fine oatmeal, and I gave unto the master of the boat a comb and a small glass: and he declared unto me, that he was bound to Pechora.

We weighed our anchors in the River Kola, and went into the sea seven or eight leagues, where we met with the wind far northerly, that of force it constrained us to go again back into the river, where came aboard of us sundry of their boats which declared unto me that they were also bound to the northwards, a-fishing for morse and salmon, and gave me liberally of their white and wheaten bread. There was one of them whose name was Gabriel, who showed me very much friendship, and he declared unto me, that all they were bound to Pechora, a-fishing for salmon and morses. He showed me by demonstrations, that with a fair wind we had seven or eight days' sailing to the River Pechora, so that I was glad of their company. This Gabriel promised to give me warning of shoals, as he did indeed.

Wednesday being Midsummer day, we sent our skiff a-land to sound the creek, where they found it almost dry at a low water. Although the harbour were evil, yet the stormy similitude of northerly winds tempted us to set our sails, and we let slip a cable and an anchor, and bare with the harbour. When we came upon the bark in the entrance of the creek, the wind did shrink so suddenly upon us, that we were not able to lead it in, and before we could have flatted the ship before the wind, we should have been on ground on the lee shore, so that we were constrained to let fall an anchor under our sails, and rode in a very breach, thinking to have warped in. Gabriel came out with his skiff, and so did sundry others also, showing their good will to help us, but all to no purpose, for they were likely to have been drowned for their labour. We rushed in upon the other small anchor that Gabriel sent aboard, and laid that anchor to seawards: and then between these two anchors we traversed the ship's head to seawards, and set our foresail and mainsail, and when the bark had way, we cut the hawser, and so got the sea to our friend.

The next high water, Gabriel and his company departed from thence.

I sent our boat on shore to fetch fresh water and wood, and at their coming on shore this Cyril welcomed our men most gently, and also banqueted them: and in the mean time caused some of his men to fill our baricoes with water, and to help our men to bear wood into their boat: and he then put on his best silk coat and his collar of pearls, and came aboard again. I bade him welcome, and gave him a dish of figs.

July. At a northwest sun we came to an anchor within half a league of the shore, where we had good plenty of fish, both haddocks and cods, riding in 10 fathom water.

Sunday our men cut wood on shore, and brought it aboard, and we ballasted our ship with stones.

This morning Gabriel saw a smoke on the way, who rowed unto it with his skiff, which smoke was two leagues from the place where we rowed: and at a northwest sun he came aboard again, and brought with him a Samoyed, which was but a young man: his apparel was then strange unto us, and he presented me with three young wild geese.

Tuesday at a northwest sun we thought that we had seen land: which afterwards proved to be a monstrous heap of ice. Within a little more than half an hour after, we first saw this ice, we were enclosed within it before we were aware of it, which was a fearful sight to see: for, for the space of six hours, it was as much as we could do to keep our ship aloof from one heap of ice, and bear room from another, with as much wind as we might bear a course.

On St James his day, at a southwest sun, there was a monstrous whale aboard of us, so near to our side that we might have thrust a sword or any other weapon in him, which we durst not do for fear he should have overthrown our ship: and then I called my company together, and all of us shouted, and with the cry that we made he departed from us: there was as much above water of his back as the breadth of our pinnace, and at his falling down, he made such a terrible noise in the water, that a man would greatly have marvelled, but God be thanked, we were quietly delivered of him. And a little after we spied certain islands, with which we bare, and found a good harbour. We came to an anchor, and named the island St James his Island, where we found fresh water.

We saw a sail coming about the point whereunder we thought to have anchored. Then I sent a skiff aboard of him, and at their coming aboard, they took acquaintance of them, and their chief man said we were past the way, which should bring us to the Ob. This land, said he, is called Novaya Zemlya, that is to say, the New Land. I gave him a steel glass, two pewter spoons, and a pair of velvet sheathed knives: he gave me 17 wild geese. This man's name was Loshak.

There were some of their company on shore, which did chase a white bear over the high cliffs into the water.

August, I met again with Loshak, and went on shore with him, and he brought me to a heap of the Samoyeds' idols, which were in number above 300, the worst and the most unartificial work that ever I saw: the eyes and mouths of sundry of them were bloody, they had the shape of men, women and children, very grossly wrought. Before certain of their idols blocks were made as high as their mouths, being all bloody, I thought that to be the table whereon they offered their sacrifices: I saw also the instruments, whereupon they had roasted flesh, and as far as I could perceive, they made their fire directly under the spit.

Loshak being there present told me that these Samoyeds were not so hurtful as they of Ob are. They have no houses, but only tents made of deer's skins, which they underprop with stakes and poles: their boats are made of deer's skins, and when they come on shore they carry their boats with them upon their backs: for their carriages they have no other beasts to serve them, but deer only. As for bread and corn they have none, except the Russians bring it to them: their knowledge is very base, for they know no letter.

Wednesday we saw a terrible heap of ice approach near to us, and therefore we thought it good with all speed to depart from thence, and so I returned to the westward again.

At night there grew so terrible a storm, that we saw not the like, although we had endured many storms since we came out of England. It was wonderful that our bark was able to brook such monstrous and terrible seas, without the great help of God, who never faileth them at need, that put their sure trust in Him.

Saturday was calm: the latitude this day at noon was 70 degrees and a tierce, we sounded here, and had nine and forty fathoms and ooze, which ooze signified that we draw toward Novaya Zemlya. And thus being out of all hope to discover any more to the eastward this year, we thought it best to return, and that for three causes. The first, the continual northeast and northerly winds. Second, because of great and terrible abundance of ice: I adventured already somewhat too far in it, but I thank God for my safe deliverance from it. Third, because the nights waxed dark, and the winter began to draw on with his storms: and therefore I resolved to take the first best wind that God should send.

September. The eleventh day we arrived at Kholmogory, and there we wintered, expecting the approach of the next summer to proceed farther in our intended discovery for the Ob.

RICHARD HAKLUYT
from *Voyages and Discoveries*

In an Open Boat

None of them knew the color of the sky. Their eyes glanced level, and were fastened upon the waves that swept toward them. These waves were of the hue of slate, save for the tops, which were of foaming white, and all of the men knew the colors of the sea. The horizon narrowed and widened, and dipped and rose, and at all times its edge was jagged with waves that seemed thrust up in points like rocks.

Many a man ought to have a bath-tub larger than the boat which here rode upon the sea. These waves were most wrongfully and barbarously abrupt and tall, and each froth-top was a problem in small-boat navigation.

The cook squatted in the bottom, and looked with both eyes at the six inches of gunwale which separated him from the ocean. His sleeves were rolled over his fat forearms, and the two flaps of his unbuttoned vest dangled as he bent to bail out the boat. Often he said, 'Gawd! that was a narrow clip.' As he remarked it he invariably gazed eastward over the broken sea.

The oiler, steering with one of the two oars in the boat, sometimes raised himself suddenly to keep clear of water that swirled in over the stern. It was a thin little oar, and it seemed often ready to snap.

The correspondent, pulling at the other oar, watched the waves and wondered why he was there.

The injured captain, lying in the bow, was at this time buried in that profound dejection and indifference which comes, temporarily at least, to even the bravest and most enduring when, willy-nilly, the firm fails, the army loses, the ship goes down. The mind of the master of a vessel is rooted deep in the timbers of her, though he command for a day or a decade; and this captain had on him the stern impression of a scene in the grays of dawn of seven turned faces, and later a stump of a topmast with a white ball on it, that slashed to and fro at the waves, went low and lower, and down. Thereafter there was something strange in his voice. Although steady, it was deep with mourning, and of a quality beyond oration or tears.

'Keep 'er a little more south, Billie,' said he.

'A little more south, sir,' said the oiler in the stern.

A seat in this boat was not unlike a seat upon a bucking broncho, and, by the same token, a broncho is not much smaller. The craft pranced and reared and plunged like an animal. As each wave came, and she rose for it, she seemed like a horse making at a fence outrageously high. The manner of her scramble over these walls of water is a mystic thing, and, moreover, at the top of them were ordinarily these problems in white water, the foam racing down from the summit of each wave, requiring a new leap, and a leap from the air. Then, after scornfully bumping a crest, she would slide and race and splash down a long incline, and arrive bobbing and nodding in front of the next menace.

A singular disadvantage of the sea lies in the fact that, after successfully surmounting one wave, you discover that there is another behind it, just as important and just as nervously anxious to do something effective in the way of swamping boats. In a ten-foot dinghy one can get an idea of the resources of the sea in the line of waves that is not probable to the average experience, which is never at sea in a dinghy. As each slaty wall of water approached, it shut all else from the view of the men in the boat, and it was not difficult to imagine that this particular wave was the final outburst of the ocean, the last effort of the grim water. There was a terrible grace in the move of the waves, and they came in silence, save for the snarling of the crests.

STEPHEN CRANE
from 'The Open Boat'

The Three Sailors [Little Billee]

There were three sailors in Bristol city,
Who took a boat and went to sea.

But first with beef and captain's biscuit,
And pickled pork they loaded she.

There was guzzling Jack and gorging Jimmy,
And the youngest he was little Bill-*ly*.

Now very soon they were so greedy,
They didn't leave not one split pea.

Says guzzling Jack to gorging Jimmy,
'I am confounded hung-*ery*.'

Says gorging Jim to guzzling Jacky,
'We have no wittles, so we must eat *we*.'

Says guzzling Jack to gorging Jimmy,
'Oh! gorging Jim, what a fool you be!'

'There's little Bill as is young and tender,
We're old and tough – so let's eat *he*.'

'Oh! Bill, we're going to kill and eat you,
So undo the collar of your chemie.'

When Bill he heard this information,
He used his pocket-handkerchie.

'Oh! let me say my catechism,
As my poor mammy taught to me.'

'Make haste, make haste,' says guzzling Jacky,
Whilst Jim pulled out his snicker-snee.

So Bill went up the maintop-gallant mast,
When down he fell on his bended knee.

He scarce had said his catechism,
When up he jumps; 'There's land I see:

'There's Jerusalem and Madagascar,
And North and South Ameri-*key*.

'There's the British fleet a-riding at anchor,
With Admiral Napier, K.C.B.'

So when they came to the Admiral's vessel,
He hanged fat Jack, and flogged Jim-*my*.

But as for little Bill, he made him
The Captain of a Seventy-three.

WILLIAM MAKEPEACE THACKERAY

Seaweed

WHEN descends on the Atlantic
    The gigantic
Storm-wind of the equinox,

Landward in his wrath he scourges
   The toiling surges,
Laden with seaweed from the rocks:

From Bermuda's reefs; from edges
   Of sunken ledges,
In some far-off, bright Azore;
From Bahama, and the dashing,
   Silver-flashing
Surges of San Salvador;

From the tumbling surf, that buries
   The Orkneyan skerries,
Answering the hoarse Hebrides;
And from wrecks of ships, and drifting
   Spars, uplifting
On the desolate, rainy seas; –

Ever drifting, drifting, drifting,
   On the shifting
Currents of the restless main;
Till in sheltered coves, and reaches
   Of sandy beaches,
All have found repose again.

So when storms of wild emotion
   Strike the ocean
Of the poet's soul, ere long
From each cave and rocky fastness,
   In its vastness,
Floats some fragment of a song:

From the far-off isles enchanted,
   Heaven has planted
With the golden fruit of Truth;
From the flashing surf, whose vision
   Gleams Elysian
In the tropic clime of Youth;

From the strong Will, and the Endeavor
   That forever
Wrestle with the tides of Fate;
From the wreck of Hopes far-scattered,
   Tempest-shattered,
Floating waste and desolate; –

Ever drifting, drifting, drifting
   On the shifting
Currents of the restless heart;
Till at length in books recorded,
   They, like hoarded
Household words, no more depart.

HENRY WADSWORTH LONGFELLOW

The Monster Pursued

Some weeks before this period I had procured a sledge and
dogs, and thus traversed the snows with inconceivable speed. I
know not whether the fiend possessed the same advantages; but
I found that, as before I had daily lost ground in the pursuit, I
now gained on him, so much so that when I first saw the ocean
he was but one day's journey in advance, and I hoped to intercept
him before he should reach the beach. With new courage,
therefore, I pressed on, and in two days arrived at a wretched

hamlet on the sea-shore. I enquired of the inhabitants concerning the fiend, and gained accurate information. A gigantic
monster, they said, had arrived the night before, armed with a
gun and many pistols; putting to flight the inhabitants of a
solitary cottage, through fear of his terrific appearance. He had
carried off their store of winter food, and, placing it in a sledge,
to draw which he had seized on a numerous drove of trained
dogs, he had harnessed them, and the same night, to the joy of
the horror-struck villagers, had pursued his journey across the
sea in a direction that led to no land; and they conjectured that
he must speedily be destroyed by the breaking of the ice, or
frozen by the eternal frosts.

On hearing this information, I suffered a temporary access
of despair. He had escaped me; and I must commence a destruc-
tive and almost endless journey across the mountainous ices of
the ocean, – amidst cold that few of the inhabitants could long
endure and which I, the native of a genial and sunny climate,
could not hope to survive. Yet at the idea that the fiend should
live and be triumphant, my rage and vengeance returned, and,
like a mighty tide, overwhelmed every other feeling. After a
slight repose, during which the spirits of the dead hovered
round, and instigated me to toil and revenge, I prepared for my
journey.

I exchanged my land-sledge for one fashioned for the
inequalities of the Frozen Ocean; and purchasing a plentiful
stock of provisions, I departed from land.

I cannot guess how many days have passed since then; but I
have endured misery, which nothing but the eternal sentiment
of a just retribution burning within my heart could have enabled
me to support. Immense and rugged mountains of ice often
barred up my passage, and I often heard the thunder of the
ground sea, which threatened my destruction. But again the
frost came, and made the paths of the sea secure.

By the quantity of provision which I had consumed, I should

guess that I had passed three weeks in this journey; and the continual protraction of hope, returning back upon the heart, often wrung bitter drops of despondency and grief from my eyes. Despair had indeed almost secured her prey, and I should soon have sunk beneath this misery. Once, after the poor animals that conveyed me had with incredible toil gained the summit of a sloping ice-mountain, and one, sinking under his fatigue, died, I viewed the expanse before me with anguish, when suddenly my eye caught a dark speck upon the dusky plain. I strained my sight to discover what it could be, and uttered a wild cry of ecstasy when I distinguished a sledge, and the distorted proportions of a well-known form within. Oh! with what a burning gush did hope revisit my heart! warm tears filled my eyes, which I hastily wiped away, that they might not intercept the view I had of the daemon; but still my sight was dimmed by the burning drops, until, giving way to the emotions that oppressed me, I wept aloud.

But this was not the time for delay: I disencumbered the dogs of their dead companion, gave them a plentiful portion of food; and, after an hour's rest, which was absolutely necessary, and yet which was bitterly irksome to me, I continued my route. The sledge was still visible; nor did I again lose sight of it, except at the moments when for a short time some ice-rock concealed it with its intervening crags. I indeed perceptibly gained on it; and when, after nearly two days' journey, I beheld my enemy at no more than a mile distant, my heart bounded within me.

But now, when I appeared almost within grasp of my foe, my hopes were suddenly extinguished, and I lost all trace of him more utterly than I had ever done before. A ground sea was heard; the thunder of its progress, as the waters rolled and swelled beneath me, became every moment more ominous and terrific. I pressed on, but in vain. The wind arose; the sea roared; and, as with the mighty shock of an earthquake, it split, and cracked with a tremendous and overwhelming sound. The work was soon finished: in a few minutes a tumultuous sea rolled between me and my enemy, and I was left drifting on a scattered piece of ice, that was continually lessening, and thus preparing for me a hideous death.

MARY SHELLEY

from *Frankenstein*

The Ever Memorable Expedition to Carthagena

Our fleet having joined another that waited for us, lay at anchor about a month in the harbour of Port-Royal in Jamaica, during which time something of consequence was certainly transacted; notwithstanding the insinuations of some who affirmed we had no business at all in that place – that in order to take the advantage of the season, proper for our enterprize, the West-Indian squadron, which had previous notice of our coming, ought to have joined us at the west-end of Hispaniola, with necessary stores and refreshments, from whence we could have sailed directly to Carthagena, before the enemy could put themselves in a good posture of defence, or indeed have an inkling of our design. Be this as it will, we sailed from Jamaica, and in ten days or a fort-night, beat up against the wind as far as the isle of Vache, with an intention, as was said, to attack the French fleet, then supposed to be lying near that place; but before we arrived they had sailed for Europe, having first dispatched an advice-boat to Carthagena with an account of our being in those seas, as also of our strength and destination. We loitered here some days longer, taking in wood, and brackish water, in the use whereof, however, our admiral seemed to consult the health of the men, by restricting each to a quart a day. At length we set sail, and arrived in a bay to the windward of Carthagena, where we came to an anchor, and lay at our ease ten days longer. Here again, certain malicious people take occasion to blame the conduct of their superiors, by saying, that in so doing, they not only unprofitably wasted time, which was very precious, considering the approach of the rainy season, but also allowed the Spaniards to recollect themselves from the terror occasioned by the approach of an English fleet, at least three times as numerous as ever appeared in that part of the world before. But if I might be allowed to give my opinion of the matter, I would ascribe this delay to the generosity of our chiefs, who scorned to take any advantage that fortune might give them, even over an enemy. At last, however, we weighed, and anchored again somewhat nearer the harbour's mouth, where we made shift to land our marines, who encamped on the beach, in despite of the enemies shot, which knocked a good many of them on the head. This piece of conduct in choosing a camp under the walls of an enemy's fortification, which I believe never happened before, was practised, I presume, with a view of accustoming the soldiers to stand fire, who were not as yet much used to discipline, most of them having been taken from the plough-tail a few months before. This expedient again has furnished matter for censure against the ministry, for sending a few raw recruits on such an important enterprize, while so many veteran regiments lay inactive at home: But surely our governors had their reasons for so doing, which possibly may be disclosed with other secrets of the deep. Perhaps they were loth to risk their best troops on such desperate service; or, the colonels and field officers of the old corps, who, generally speaking, enjoyed their commissions as sine-cures or pensions, for some domestic services tendered to the court, refused to embark in such a dangerous and precarious undertaking; for which refusal, no doubt, they are to be much commended.

TOBIAS SMOLLETT
from *Roderick Random*

'Now overhead a rainbow, bursting through'

Now overhead a rainbow, bursting through
  The scattering clouds, shone, spanning the dark sea,
Resting its bright base on the quivering blue,
  And all within its arch appeared to be
Clearer than that without, and its wide hue
  Waxed broad and waving, like a banner free,
Then changed like to a bow that's bent, and then
Forsook the dim eyes of these shipwrecked men.

It changed of course – a heavenly chameleon,
  The airy child of vapour and the sun,
Brought forth in purple, cradled in vermilion,
  Baptized in molten gold and swathed in dun,
Glittering like crescents o'er a Turk's pavilion
  And blending every colour into one,
Just like a black eye in a recent scuffle
(For sometimes we must box without the muffle).

Our shipwrecked seamen thought it a good omen;
  It is as well to think so now and then.
'Twas an old custom of the Greek and Roman,
  And may become of great advantage when
Folks are discouraged; and most surely no men
  Had greater need to nerve themselves again
Than these, and so this rainbow looked like hope,
Quite a celestial kaleidoscope.

About this time a beautiful white bird,
  Webfooted, not unlike a dove in size
And plumage (probably it might have erred
  Upon its course), passed oft before their eyes

And tried to perch, although it saw and heard
  The men within the boat, and in this guise
It came and went and fluttered round them till
Night fell. This seemed a better omen still.

But in this case I also must remark,
  'Twas well this bird of promise did not perch,
Because the tackle of our shattered bark
  Was not so safe for roosting as a church,
And had it been the dove from Noah's ark,
  Returning there from her successful search,
Which in their way that moment chanced to fall,
They would have eat her, olive branch and all.

With twilight it again came on to blow,
  But not with violence. The stars shone out,
The boat made way; yet now they were so low
  They knew not where nor what they were about.
Some fancied they saw land, and some said, 'No!'
  The frequent fog banks gave them cause to doubt.
Some swore that they heard breakers, others guns,
And all mistook about the latter once.

As morning broke the light wind died away,
  When he who had the watch sung out and swore,
If 'twas not land that rose with the sun's ray,
  He wished that land he never might see more.
And the rest rubbed their eyes and saw a bay
  Or thought they saw, and shaped their course for shore,
For shore it was and gradually grew
Distinct and high and palpable to view.

And then of these some part burst into tears,
  And others, looking with a stupid stare,
Could not yet separate their hopes from fears
  And seemed as if they had no further care,
While a few prayed (the first time for some years).
  And at the bottom of the boat three were
Asleep; they shook them by the hand and head
And tried to awaken them, but found them dead.

The day before, fast sleeping on the water,
  They found a turtle of the hawksbill kind,
And by good fortune gliding softly, caught her,
  Which yielded a day's life and to their mind
Proved even still a more nutritious matter,
  Because it left encouragement behind.
They thought that in such perils more than chance
Had sent them this for their deliverance.

The land appeared a high and rocky coast,
  And higher grew the mountains as they drew,
Set by a current, toward it. They were lost
  In various conjectures, for none knew
To what part of the earth they had been tost,
  So changeable had been the winds that blew.
Some thought it was Mount Etna, some the highlands
Of Candia, Cyprus, Rhodes, or other islands.

Meantime the current, with a rising gale,
  Still set them onwards to the welcome shore,
Like Charon's bark of spectres, dull and pale.
  Their living freight was now reduced to four,

And three dead, whom their strength could not avail
  To heave into the deep with those before,
Though the two sharks still followed them and dashed
The spray into their faces as they splashed.

Famine, despair, cold, thirst, and heat had done
  Their work on them by turns, and thinned them to
Such things a mother had not known her son
  Amidst the skeletons of that gaunt crew.
By night chilled, by day scorched, thus one by one
  They perished, until withered to these few,
But chiefly by a species of self-slaughter,
In washing down Pedrillo with salt water.

As they drew nigh the land, which now was seen
  Unequal in its aspect here and there,
They felt the freshness of its growing green,
  That waved in forest-tops and smoothed the air,
And fell upon their glazed eyes like a screen
  From glistening waves and skies so hot and bare.
Lovely seemed any object that should sweep
Away the vast, salt, dread, eternal deep.

The shore looked wild without a trace of man
  And girt by formidable waves; but they
Were mad for land, and thus their course they ran,
  Though right ahead the roaring breakers lay.
A reef between them also now began
  To show its boiling surf and bounding spray,
But finding no place for their landing better,
They ran the boat for shore and overset her.

GEORGE GORDON, LORD BYRON
from *Don Juan*, Canto II

The Wonders of Coral

APRIL 12TH – In the morning, we stood out of the Lagoon. I am glad we have visited these islands: such formations surely rank high amongst the wonderful objects of this world. It is not a wonder, which at first strikes the eye of the body, but rather, after reflection, the eye of reason. We feel surprised, when travellers relate accounts of the vast extent of certain ancient ruins; but how utterly insignificant are the greatest of these, when compared to the pile of stone here accumulated by the work of various minute animals. Throughout the whole group of islands, every single atom, even from the smallest particle to large fragments of rock, bears the stamp of having been subjected to the power of organic arrangement. Captain FitzRoy, at the distance of but little more than a mile from the shore, sounded with a line, 7,200 feet long, and found no bottom. This island is, therefore, a lofty submarine mountain, which has a greater inclination than even those of volcanic origin on the land.

CHARLES DARWIN
from *Voyage of the* Beagle

The Pacific Atoll

ABOUT four in the morning, as the captain and Herrick sat together on the rail, there arose from the midst of the night in front of them the voice of breakers. Each sprang to his feet and stared and listened. The sound was continuous, like the passing of a train; no rise or fall could be distinguished; minute by minute the ocean heaved with an equal potency against the invisible isle; and as time passed, and Herrick waited in vain for any vicissitude in the volume of that roaring, a sense of the eternal weighed upon his mind. To the expert eye the isle itself was to be inferred from a certain string of blots along the starry heaven. And the schooner was laid to and anxiously observed till daylight.

There was little or no morning bank. A brightening came in the east; then a wash of some ineffable, faint, nameless hue between crimson and silver; and then coals of fire. These glimmered a while on the sea-line, and seemed to brighten and darken and spread out, and still the night and the stars reigned undisturbed; it was as though a speck should catch and glow and creep along the foot of some heavy and almost incombustible wall-hanging, and the room itself be scarce menaced. Yet a little after, and the whole east glowed with gold and scarlet, and the hollow of heaven was filled with the daylight.

The isle – the undiscovered, the scarce-believed in – now lay before them and close aboard; and Herrick thought that never in his dreams had he beheld anything more strange and delicate. The beach was excellently white, the continuous barrier of trees inimitably green; the land perhaps ten feet high, the trees thirty more. Every here and there, as the schooner coasted northward, the wood was intermitted; and he could see clear over the inconsiderable strip of land (as a man looks over a wall) to the lagoon within – and clear over that again to where the far side of the atoll prolonged its pencilling of trees against the morning sky. He tortured himself to find analogies. The isle was like the rim of a great vessel sunken in the waters; it was like the embankment of an annular railway grown upon with wood: so slender it seemed amidst the outrageous breakers, so frail and pretty, he would scarce have wondered to see it sink and disappear without a sound, and the waves close smoothly over its descent.

ROBERT LOUIS STEVENSON
from *The Ebb-Tide*

Drifting

A typhoon was coming; and I sat on the sea-wall in a great wind
to look at the breakers; and old Amano Jinsuké sat beside me.
Southeast all was black-blue gloom, except the sea, which had a
strange and tawny color. Enormous surges were already towering
in. A hundred yards away they crumbled over with thunder and
earthquake, and sent their foam leaping and sheeting up the
slope, to spring at our faces. After each long crash, the sound
of the shingle retreating was exactly like the roar of a railway
train at full speed. I told Amano Jinsuké that it made me afraid;
and he smiled.

'I swam for two nights and two days,' he said, 'in a sea worse
than this. I was nineteen years old at the time. Out of a crew of
eight, I was the only man saved.

'Our ship was called the *Fukuju Maru*; she was owned by
Mayéda Jingorō, of this town! All of the crew but one were
Yaidzu men. The captain was Saito Kichiyémon, a man more
than sixty years of age; he lived in Jō-no-Koshi – the street just
behind us. There was another old man on board, called Nito
Shōshichi, who lived in the Araya quarter. Then there was Terao
Kankichi, forty-two years old; his brother Minosuké, a lad of
sixteen, was also with us. The Terao folk lived in Araya. Then
there was Saito Heikichi, thirty years old; and there was a man
called Matsushirō; he came from Suō, but had settled in Yaidzu.
Washino Otokichi was another of the crew; he lived in Jō-no-
Koshi, and was only twenty-one. I was the youngest on board
– excepting Terao Minosuké.

'We sailed from Yaidzu on the morning of the tenth day of
the seventh month of Manyen Gwannen – the Year of the Ape
– bound for Sanuki. On the night of the eleventh, in the Kishū
offing, we were caught by a typhoon from the southeast. A little
before midnight, the ship capsized. As I felt her going over, I

caught a plank, and threw it out, and jumped. It was blowing fearfully at the time; and the night was so dark that I could see only a few feet away; but I was lucky enough to find that plank, and put it under me. In another moment the ship was gone. Near me in the water were Washino Otokichi and the Terao brothers and the man Matsushirō – all swimming. There was no sign of the rest: they probably went down with the ship. We five kept calling to each other as we went up and down with the great seas; and I found that everyone except Terao Kankichi had a plank or a timber of some sort. I cried to Kankichi: "Elder brother, you have children, and I am very young – let me give you this plank!" He shouted back: "In this sea a plank is dangerous! Keep away from timber, Jinyō! – you may get hurt!" Before I could answer him, a wave like a black mountain burst over us. I was a long time under; and when I came up again, there was no sign of Kankichi. The younger men were still swimming; but they had been swept away to the left of me; I could not see them. We shouted to each other. I tried to keep with the waves – the others called to me: "Jinyō! Jinyō! come this way – this way!" But I knew that to go in their direction would be very dangerous; for every time that a wave struck me sideways, I was taken under. So I called back to them: "Keep with the tide! – keep with the current!" But they did not seem to understand; and they still called to me: "Kocchi é koi! – kocchi é koi!" – and their voices each time sounded more and more far away. I became afraid to answer . . . The drowned call to you like that when they want company: Kocchi é koi! – kocchi é koi! . . .

'After a little time the calling ceased; and I heard only the sea and the wind and the rain. It was so dark that one could see the waves only at the moment they went by – high black shadows, each with a great pull. By the pull of them I guessed how to direct myself. The rain kept them from breaking much; had it not been for the rain, no man could have lived long in such a sea. And hour after hour the wind became worse, and the swells grew higher; and I prayed for help to Jizō-Sama of Ogawa all that night . . . Lights? – yes, there were lights in the water, but not many: the large kind, that shine like candles . . .

'At dawn the sea looked ugly – a muddy green; and the waves were like hills; and the wind was terrible. Rain and spray made a fog over the water; and there was no horizon. But even if there had been land in sight I could have done nothing except try to keep afloat. I felt hungry – very hungry; and the pain of the hunger soon became hard to bear. All that day I went up and down with the great waves – drifting under the wind and the rain; and there was no sign of land. I did not know where I was going: under that sky one could not tell east from west.

'After dark the wind lulled; but the rain still poured, and all was black. The pain of the hunger passed; but I felt weak – so weak that I thought I must go under. Then I heard the voices calling me, just as they had called me the night before: "Kocchi é koi! – kocchi é koi!" . . . And all at once, I saw the four men of the *Fukuju Maru* – not swimming, but standing by me – Terao Kankichi, and Terao Minosuké and Washino Otokichi, and the man Matsushirō. All looked at me with angry faces; and the boy Minosuké cried out, as in reproach: "Here I have to fix the helm; and you, Jinsuké, do nothing but sleep!" Then Terao Kankichi – the one to whom I had offered the plank – bent over me with a kakemono in his hands, and half-unrolled it, and said: "Jinyō! here I have a picture of Amida Buddha – see! Now indeed you must repeat the *Nembutsu!*" He spoke strangely, in a way that made me afraid: I looked at the figure of the Buddha; and I repeated the prayer in great fear – "Namu Amida Butsu! – namu Amida Butsu!" In the same moment a pain, like the pain of fire, stung through my thighs and hips; and I found that I had rolled off the plank into the sea. The pain had been caused by a great katsu-no-éboshi . . . You never saw a katsuo-no-éboshi? It is a jelly-fish shaped like the éboshi, or cap, of a Shintō priest; and we call it the katsuo-no-éboshi because the katsuo-fish [bonito] feed upon it. When that thing appears anywhere, the fishermen expect to catch many katsuo. The body is clear like glass; but underneath there is a kind of purple fringe, and long purple strings; and when those strings touch you, the pain is very great, and lasts for a long time . . . That pain revived me; if I had not been stung I might never have awakened. I got on the plank again, and prayed to Jizō-Sama of Ogawa, and to Kompira-Sama; and I was able to keep awake until morning.

'Before daylight the rain stopped, and the sky began to clear; for I could see some stars. At dawn I got drowsy again; and I was awakened by a blow on the head. A large sea-bird had struck me. The sun was rising behind clouds; and the waves had become gentle. Presently a small brown bird flew by my face, a coast-bird (I do not know its real name); and I thought that there must be land in sight. I looked behind me, and I saw mountains. I did not recognize the shapes of them: they were blue – seemed to be nine or ten *ri* distant. I made up my mind to paddle towards them, though I had little hope of getting to shore. I was feeling hungry again – terribly hungry!

'I paddled toward the mountains, hour after hour. Once more I fell asleep; and once again a sea-bird struck me. All day I paddled. Toward evening I could tell, from the look of the mountains, that I was approaching them; but I knew that it would take me two days to reach the shore. I had almost ceased to hope when I caught sight of a ship, a big junk. She was sailing toward me; but I saw that, unless I could swim faster, she would pass me at a great distance. It was my last chance: so I dropped the plank, and swam as fast as I could. I did get within about two chō of her: then I shouted. But I could see nobody on deck; and I got no answer. In another minute she had passed beyond me. The sun was setting; and I despaired. All of a sudden a man came on deck, and shouted to me: "Don't try to swim! don't tire yourself – we are going to send a boat!" I saw the sail lowered at the same time; and I felt so glad that new strength seemed to come to me; I swam on fast. Then the junk dropped a little boat; and as the boat came toward me, a man called out: "Is there anybody else? – have you dropped anything?" I answered: "I had nothing but a plank" . . . In the same instant all my strength was gone: I felt the men in the boat pulling me up; but I could neither speak nor move, and everything became dark.

'After a time I heard the voices again – the voices of the men of the *Fukujō Maru*: "Jinyō! Jinyō!" – and I was frightened. Then somebody shook me, and said: "*Oi! oi!* it is only a dream!" – and I saw that I was lying in the junk, under a hanging lantern (for it was night); and beside me an old man, a stranger, was kneeling, with a cup of boiled rice in his hand. "Try to eat a little," he said, very kindly. I wanted to sit up, but could not; then he fed me himself, out of the cup. When it was empty I asked for more; but the old man answered: "Not now; you must sleep first." I heard him say to someone else: "Give him nothing more until I tell you: if you let him eat much, he will die." I slept again; and twice more that night I was given rice – soft-boiled rice – one small cupful at a time.

'In the morning I felt much better; and the old man, who had brought me the rice, came and questioned me. When he heard about the loss of our ship, and the time that I had been in the water, he expressed great pity for me. He told me that I had drifted, in those two nights and days, more than twenty-five *ri*. "We went after your plank," he said, "and picked it up. Perhaps you would like to present it some day to the temple of Kompira-Sama." I thanked him, but answered that I wanted to offer it to the temple of Jizō-Sama of Ogawa, at Yaidzu; for it was to Jizō-Sama of Ogawa that I had most often prayed for help.

'The kind old man was the captain, and also the owner, of

the junk. She was a Banshū ship, and was bound for the port of Kuki, in Kishū ... You write the name, Ku-ki, with the character for "demon" – so that it means the Nine Demons ... All the men of the ship were very good to me. I was naked, except for a loincloth, when I came on board; and they found clothes for me. One gave me an under-robe, and another an upper-robe, and another a girdle; several gave me towels and sandals; and all of them together made up a gift of money for me, amounting to between six and seven ryō.

'When we reached Kuki – a nice little place, though it has a queer name – the captain took me to a good inn; and after a few days' rest I got strong again. Then the governor of the district, the Jitō, as we called him in those days, sent for me, and heard my story, and had it written down. He told me that he would have to send a report of the matter to the Jitō of the Yaidzu district, after which he would find means to send me home. But the Banshū captain who had saved me offered to take me home in his own ship, and also to act as messenger for the Jitō, and there was much argument between the two. At that time we had no telegraph and no post; and to send a special messenger (hikyaku), from Kuki to Yaidzu, would have cost at least fifty ryō. But, on the other hand, there were particular laws and customs about such matters – laws very different from those of today. Meanwhile a Yaidzu ship came to the neighboring port of Arasha; and a woman of Kuki, who happened to be at Arasha, told the Yaidzu captain that I was at Kuki. The Yaidzu ship then came to Kuki; and the Jitō decided to send me home in charge of the Yaidzu captain, giving him a written order.

'Altogether, it was about a month from the time of the loss of the *Fukuju Maru* when I returned to Yaidzu. We reached the harbor at night; and I did not go home at once: it would have frightened my people. Although no certain news of the loss of our ship had then been received at Yaidzu, several things belonging to her had been picked up by fishing-craft; and as the typhoon had come very suddenly, with a terrible sea, it was generally believed that the *Fukuju Maru* had gone down, and that all of us had been drowned . . . None of the other men were ever heard of again . . . I went that night to the house of a friend; and in the morning I sent word to my parents and brother; and they came for me . . .

'Once every year I go to the temple of Kompira in Sanuki: all who have been saved from shipwreck go there to give thanks. And I often go to the temple of Jizō-Sama of Ogawa. If you will come with me there tomorrow, I will show you that plank.'

LAFCADIO HEARN

The Castaway

Obscurest night involved the sky,
    The Atlantic billows roared,
When such a destined wretch as I
    Washed headlong from on board
Of friends, of hope, of all bereft,
His floating home for ever left.

No braver chief could Albion boast
    Than he with whom he went,
Nor ever ship left Albion's coast
    With warmer wishes sent,
He loved them both, but both in vain,
Nor him beheld, nor her again.

Not long beneath the whelming brine
    Expert to swim, he lay,
Nor soon he felt his strength decline
    Or courage die away;
But waged with Death a lasting strife
Supported by despair of life.

He shouted, nor his friends had failed
    To check the vessel's course,
But so the furious blast prevailed
    That, pitiless perforce,
They left their outcast mate behind,
And scudded still before the wind.

Some succour yet they could afford,
    And, such as storms allow,
The cask, the coop, the floated cord
    Delayed not to bestow;
But he, they knew, nor ship or shore,
Whate'er they gave, should visit more.

Nor, cruel as it seemed, could he
    Their haste, himself, condemn,
Aware that flight in such a sea
    Alone could rescue *them*;
Yet bitter felt it still to die
Deserted, and his friends so nigh.

He long survives who lives an hour
    In ocean, self-upheld,
And so long he with unspent power
    His destiny repelled,
And ever, as the minutes flew,
Entreated help, or cried, Adieu!

At length, his transient respite past,
    His comrades, who before
Had heard his voice in every blast,
    Could catch the sound no more;
For then, by toil subdued, he drank
The stifling wave, and then he sank.

No poet wept him, but the page
    Of narrative sincere
That tells his name, his worth, his age,
    Is wet with Anson's tear,
And tears by bards or heroes shed
Alike immortalise the dead.

I, therefore, purpose not or dream,
    Descanting on his fate,
To give the melancholy theme
    A more enduring date,
But misery still delights to trace
Its semblance in another's case.

No voice divine the storm allayed,
    No light propitious shone,
When, snatched from all effectual aid,
    We perished, each, alone;
But I, beneath a rougher sea,
And whelmed in deeper gulfs than he.

WILLIAM COWPER

'Where lies the Land to which yon
Ship must go?'

Where lies the Land to which yon Ship must go?
Fresh as a lark mounting at break of day,
Festively she puts forth in trim array;
Is she for tropic suns, or polar snow?
What boots the inquiry? – Neither friend nor foe
She cares for; let her travel where she may,
She finds familiar names, a beaten way
Ever before her, and a wind to blow.
Yet still I ask, what haven is her mark?
And, almost as it was when ships were rare,
(From time to time, like Pilgrims, here and there
Crossing the waters) doubt, and something dark,
Of the old Sea some reverential fear,
Is with me at thy farewell, joyous Bark!

WILLIAM WORDSWORTH

'Thus with imagined wing . . .'

Thus with imagined wing our swift scene flies
In motion of no less celerity
Than that of thought. Suppose that you have seen
The well-appointed King at Hampton pier
Embark his royalty, and his brave fleet
With silken streamers the young Phoebus fanning.
Play with your fancies, and in them behold
Upon the hempen tackle ship-boys climbing;
Hear the shrill whistle which doth order give
To sounds confused; behold the threaden sails,

Borne with th'invisible and creeping wind,
Draw the huge bottoms through the furrowed sea,
Breasting the lofty surge. O, do but think
You stand upon the rivage and behold
A city on th'inconstant billows dancing;
For so appears this fleet majestical,
Holding due course to Harfleur. Follow, follow!
Grapple your minds to sternage of this navy,
And leave your England, as dead midnight still,
Guarded with grandsires, babies, and old women,
Either past or not arrived to pith and puissance.
For who is he whose chin is but enriched
With one appearing hair that will not follow
These culled and choice-drawn cavaliers to France?

WILLIAM SHAKESPEARE
from *Henry V*, III, Prologue

The Loss of the Brig

By this time, now and then sheering to one side or the other to avoid a reef, but still hugging the wind and the land, we had got round Iona and begun to come alongside Mull. The tide at the tail of the land ran very strong, and threw the brig about. Two hands were put to the helm, and Hoseason himself would sometimes lend a help; and it was strange to see three strong men throw their weight upon the tiller, and it (like a living thing) struggle against and drive them back. This would have been the greater danger, had not the sea been for some while free of obstacles. Mr Riach, besides, announced from the top that he saw clear water ahead.

'Ye were right,' said Hoseason to Alan. 'Ye have saved the brig, sir; I'll mind that when we come to clear accounts.' And

I believe he not only meant what he said, but would have done it; so high a place did the *Covenant* hold in his affections.

But this is matter only for conjecture, things having gone otherwise than he forecast.

'Keep her away a point,' sings out Mr Riach. 'Reef to windward!'

And just at the same time the tide caught the brig, and threw the wind out of her sails. She came round into the wind like a top, and the next moment struck the reef with such a dunch as threw us all flat upon the deck, and came near to shake Mr Riach from his place upon the mast.

I was on my feet in a minute. The reef on which we had struck was close in under the south-west end of Mull, off a little isle they called Earraid, which lay low and black upon the larboard. Sometimes the swell broke clean over us; sometimes it only ground the poor brig upon the reef, so that we could hear her beat herself to pieces; and what with the great noise of the sails, and the singing of the wind, and the flying of the spray in the moonlight, and the sense of danger, I think my head must have been partly turned, for I could scarcely understand the things I saw . . .

We had one of the wounded men told off to keep a watch upon the seas and cry us warning. Well, we had the boat about ready to be launched, when this man sang out pretty shrill: 'For God's sake, hold on!' We knew by his tone that it was something more than ordinary; and sure enough, there followed a sea so huge that it lifted the brig right up and canted her over on her beam. Whether the cry came too late or my hold was too weak, I know not; but at the sudden tilting of the ship I was cast clean over the bulwarks into the sea.

I went down, and drank my fill; and then came up, and got a blink of the moon; and then down again. They say a man sinks the third time for good. I cannot be made like other folk, then; for I would not like to write how often I went down or how often I came up again. All the while, I was being hurled along, and beaten upon and choked, and then swallowed whole; and the thing was so distracting to my wits, that I was neither sorry nor afraid.

Presently, I found I was holding to a spar, which helped me somewhat. And then all of a sudden I was in quiet water, and began to come to myself.

It was the spare yard I had got hold of, and I was amazed to see how far I had travelled from the brig. I hailed her, indeed; but it was plain she was already out of cry. She was still holding together; but whether or not they had yet launched the boat, I was too far off and too low down to see.

While I was hailing the brig, I spied a tract of water lying between us, where no great waves came, but which yet boiled white all over and bristled in the moon with rings and bubbles. Sometimes the whole tract swung to one side, like the tail of a live serpent; sometimes, for a glimpse, it all would disappear and then boil up again. What it was I had no guess, which for the time increased my fear of it; but I now know it must have been the roost or tide race, which had carried me away so fast and tumbled me about so cruelly, and at last, as if tired of that play, had flung out me and the spare yard upon its landward margin.

I now lay quite becalmed, and began to feel that a man can die of cold as well as of drowning. The shores of Erraid were close in; I could see in the moonlight the dots of heather and the sparkling of the mica in the rocks.

'Well,' thought I to myself, 'if I cannot get as far as that, it's strange!'

I had no skill of swimming, Essen water being small in our neighbourhood; but when I laid hold upon the yard with both arms, and kicked out with both feet, I soon begun to find that I was moving. Hard work it was, and mortally slow; but in about an hour of kicking and splashing, I had got well in between the points of a sandy bay surrounded by low hills.

The sea was here quite quiet; there was no sound of any surf; the moon shone clear; and I thought in my heart I had never seen a place so desert and desolate. But it was dry land; and when at last it grew so shallow that I could leave the yard and wade ashore upon my feet, I cannot tell if I was more tired or more grateful. Both at least, I was: tired as I never was before that night; and grateful to God as I trust I have been often, though never with more cause.

ROBERT LOUIS STEVENSON
from *Kidnapped*

The Isle of Muck

Among other guests, which the hospitality of Dunvegan brought to the table, a visit was paid by the laird and lady of a small island south of Sky, of which the proper name is Muack, which signifies swine. It is commonly called Muck, which the proprietor not liking, has endeavoured, without effect, to change to Monk. It is usual to call gentlemen in Scotland by the name of their possessions, as Raasay, Bernera, Loch Buy, a practice necessary in countries inhabited by clans, where all that live in the same territory have one name, and must be therefore discriminated by some addition. This gentleman, whose name, I think, is Maclean, should be regularly called Muck; but the appellation, which he thinks too coarse for his island, he would like still less for himself, and he is therefore addressed by the title of, Isle of Muck.

This little island, however it be named, is of considerable value. It is two English miles long, and three quarters of a mile broad, and consequently contains only nine hundred and sixty English acres. It is chiefly arable. Half of this little dominion the laird retains in his own hand, and on the other half, live one hundred and sixty persons, who pay their rent by exported corn. What rent they pay, we were not told, and could not decently inquire. The proportion of the people to the land is such, as the most fertile countries do not commonly maintain.

The laird having all his people under his immediate view, seems to be very attentive to their happiness. The devastation of the small-pox, when it visits places where it comes seldom, is well known. He has disarmed it of its terrour at Muack, by inoculating eighty of his people. The expence was two shillings and sixpence a head. Many trades they cannot have among them, but upon occasion, he fetches a smith from the Isle of Egg, and has a tailor from the main land, six times a year. This island well deserved to be seen, but the laird's absence left us no opportunity.

Every inhabited island has its appendant and subordinate islets. Muck, however small, has yet others smaller about it, one of which has only ground sufficient to afford pasture for three wethers.

At Dunvegan I had tasted lotus, and was in danger of forgetting that I was ever to depart, till Mr Boswell sagely reproached me with my sluggishness and softness. I had no very forcible defence to make; and we agreed to pursue our journey.

SAMUEL JOHNSON
from *Journey to the Western Islands of Scotland*

Rock Rodondo

'For they this hight The Rocke of *vile* Reproch,
A daungerous and dreadful place,
To which nor fish nor fowle did once approach,

But yelling Meawes, with Seagulles hoarse and bace,
And Cormoyrants, with birds of ravenous race,
Which still sate waiting on that dreadful clift.'

~ ~ ~

'With that the rolling sea resounding soft,
In his big base them fitly answered,
And on the rocke the waves breaking aloft,
A solemne Meane unto them measured.'

~ ~ ~

'Then he the boatemen bad row easily,
And let him heare some part of that rare melody.'

~ ~ ~

'Suddeinly an innumerable flight
Of harmefull fowles about them fluttering, cride,
And with their wicked wings them oft did smight,
And sore annoyed, groping in that griesly night.'

~ ~ ~

'Even all the nation of unfortunate
And fatall birds about them flocked were.'

To go up into a high stone tower is not only a very fine thing in itself, but the very best mode of gaining a comprehensive view of the region round about. It is all the better if this tower stand solitary and alone, like that mysterious Newport one, or else be sole survivor of some perished castle.

Now, with reference to the Enchanted Isles, we are fortunately supplied with just such a noble point of observation in a remarkable rock, from its peculiar figure called of old by the Spaniards, Rock Rodondo, or Round Rock. Some two hundred and fifty feet high, rising straight from the sea ten miles from land, with the whole mountainous group to the south and east, Rock Rodondo occupies, on a large scale, very much the position which the famous Campanile or detached Bell Tower of St Mark does with respect to the tangled group of hoary edifices around it.

Ere ascending, however, to gaze abroad upon the Encantadas, this sea-tower itself claims attention. It is visible at the distance of thirty miles; and, fully participating in that enchantment which pervades the group, when first seen afar invariably is mistaken for a sail. Four leagues away, of a golden, hazy noon, it seems some Spanish Admiral's ship, stacked up with glittering canvas. Sail ho! Sail ho! Sail ho! from all three masts. But coming nigh, the enchanted frigate is transformed apace into a craggy keep.

My first visit to the spot was made in the gray of the morning. With a view of fishing, we had lowered three boats, and pulling some two miles from our vessel, found ourselves just before dawn of day close under the moon-shadow of Rodondo. Its aspect was heightened, and yet softened, by the strange double twilight of the hour. The great full moon burnt in the low west like a half-spent beacon, casting a soft mellow tinge upon the sea like that cast by a waning fire of embers upon a midnight hearth; while along the entire east the invisible sun sent pallid intimations of his coming. The wind was light; the waves languid; the stars twinkled with a faint effulgence; all nature seemed supine with the long night watch, and half-suspended in jaded expectation of the sun. This was the critical hour to catch Rodondo in his perfect mood. The twilight was just enough to reveal every striking point, without tearing away the dim investiture of wonder.

From a broken stair-like base, washed, as the steps of a water-palace, by the waves, the tower rose in entablatures of strata to a shaven summit. These uniform layers, which compose the mass, form its most peculiar feature. For at their lines of junction they project flatly into encircling shelves, from top to bottom, rising one above another in graduated series. And as the eaves of any old barn or abbey are alive with swallows, so were all these rocky ledges with unnumbered sea-fowl. Eaves upon eaves, and nests upon nests. Here and there were long birdlime streaks of a ghostly white staining the tower from sea to air, readily accounting for its sail-like look afar. All would have been bewitchingly quiescent, were it not for the demoniac din created by the birds. Not only were the eaves rustling with them, but they flew densely overhead, spreading themselves into a winged and continually shifting canopy. The tower is the resort of aquatic birds for hundreds of leagues around. To the north, to the east, to the west, stretches nothing but eternal ocean; so that the man-of-war hawk coming from the coasts of North America, Polynesia, or Peru, makes his first land at Rodondo. And yet though Rodondo be terra-firma, no landbird ever lighted on it. Fancy a red-robin or a canary there! What a falling into the hands of the Philistines, when the poor warbler should be surrounded by such locust-flights of strong bandit birds, with long bills cruel as daggers.

I know not where one can better study the Natural History of strange sea-fowl than at Rodondo. It is the aviary of Ocean. Birds light here which never touched mast or tree; hermit-birds, which ever fly alone; cloud-birds, familiar with unpierced zones of air.

Let us first glance low down to the lowermost shelf of all, which is the widest, too, and but a little space from high-water mark. What outlandish beings are these? Erect as men, but hardly as symmetrical, they stand all round the rock like sculptured caryatides, supporting the next range of caves above. Their bodies are grotesquely misshapen; their bills short; their feet seemingly legless; while the members at their sides are neither fin, wing, nor arm. And truly neither fish, flesh, nor fowl is the penguin; as an edible, pertaining neither to Carnival nor Lent; without exception the most ambiguous and least lovely creature yet discovered by man. Though dabbling in all three elements, and indeed possessing some rudimental claims to all, the penguin is at home in none. On land it stumps; afloat it sculls; in the air it flops. As if ashamed of her failure, Nature keeps this ungainly child hidden away at the ends of the earth, in the Straits of Magellan, and on the abased sea-story of Rodondo.

But look, what are yon wobegone regiments drawn up on the next shelf above? what rank and file of large strange fowl? what sea Friars of Orders Gray? Pelicans. Their elongated bills, and heavy leathern pouches suspended thereto, give them the most lugubrious expression. A pensive race, they stand for hours together without motion. Their dull, ashy plumage imparts an aspect as if they had been powdered over with cinders. A penitential bird, indeed, fitly haunting the shores of the clinkered Encantadas, whereon tormented Job himself might have well sat down and scraped himself with potsherds.

Higher up now we mark the gony, or gray albatross, anomalously so called, an unsightly, unpoetic bird, unlike its storied kinsman, which is the snow-white ghost of the haunted Capes of Hope and Horn.

As we still ascend from shelf to shelf, we find the tenants of the tower serially disposed in order of their magnitude: – gannets, black and speckled haglets, jays, sea-hens, sperm-whale-birds, gulls of all varieties: – thrones, princedoms, powers, dominating one above another in senatorial array; while, sprinkled over all, like an ever-repeated fly in a great piece of broidery, the stormy petrel or Mother Cary's chicken sounds his continual challenge and alarm. That this mysterious humming-bird of ocean – which, had it but brilliancy of hue, might, from its evanescent liveliness, be almost called its butterfly, yet whose chirrup under the stern is ominous to mariners as to the peasant the death-tick sounding from behind the chimney jamb – should have its special haunt at the Encantadas, contributes, in the seaman's mind, not a little to their dreary spell.

As day advances the dissonant din augments. With ear-splitting cries the wild birds celebrate their matins. Each moment, flights push from the tower, and join the aerial choir hovering overhead, while their places below are supplied by darting myriads. But down through all this discord of commotion, I hear clear, silver, bugle-like notes unbrokenly falling, like oblique lines of swift-slanting rain in a cascading shower. I gaze far up, and behold a snow-white angelic thing, with one long, lance-like feather thrust out behind. It is the bright, inspiriting chanticleer of ocean, the beauteous bird, from its bestirring whistle of musical invocation, fitly styled the 'Boatswain's Mate.'

The winged, life-clouding Rodondo had its full counterpart in the finny hosts which peopled the waters at its base. Below the water-line, the rock seemed one honey-comb of grottoes, affording labyrinthine lurking-places for swarms of fairy fish. All were strange; many exceedingly beautiful; and would have well graced the costliest glass globes in which gold-fish are kept for a show. Nothing was more striking than the complete novelty of many individuals of this multitude. Here hues were seen as yet unpainted, and figures which are unengraved.

To show the multitude, avidity, and nameless fearlessness and tameness of these fish, let me say, that often, marking through clear spaces of water – temporarily made so by the concentric dartings of the fish above the surface – certain larger and less unwary wights, which swam slow and deep; our anglers would cautiously essay to drop their lines down to these last. But in vain; there was no passing the uppermost zone. No sooner did the hook touch the sea, than a hundred infatuates contended for the honor of capture. Poor fish of Rodondo! in your victimized confidence, you are of the number of those who inconsiderately trust, while they do not understand, human nature.

But the dawn is now fairly day. Band after band, the sea-fowl sail away to forage the deep for their food. The tower is left solitary, save the fish-caves at its base. Its bird-lime gleams in the golden rays like the whitewash of a tall light-house, or the lofty sails of a cruiser. This moment, doubtless, while we know it to be a dead desert rock, other voyagers are taking oaths it is a glad populous ship.

But ropes now, and let us ascend. Yet soft, this is not so easy.

HERMAN MELVILLE
from 'Las Encantadas'

An Albatross

This day we saw the last of the albatrosses, which had been our companions a great part of the time off the Cape. I had been interested in the bird from descriptions which I had read of it, and was not at all disappointed. We caught one or two with a baited hook which we floated astern upon a shingle. Their long, flapping wings, long legs, and large, staring eyes, give them a very peculiar appearance. They look well on the wing; but one of the finest sights that I have ever seen, was an albatross asleep upon the water, during a calm, off Cape Horn, when a heavy sea was running. There being no breeze, the surface of the water was unbroken, but a long, heavy swell was rolling, and we saw the fellow, all white, directly ahead of us, asleep upon the waves, with his head under his wing; now rising on the top of a huge billow, and then falling slowly until he was lost in the hollow between. He was undisturbed for some time, until the noise of our bows, gradually approaching roused him, when, lifting his head, he stared upon us for a moment, and then spread his wide wings and took his flight.

RICHARD HENRY DANA, JR.
from *Two Years before the Mast*

'The breezes blew, the
white foam flew'

The breezes blew, the white foam flew,
    The furrow follow'd free:
We were the first that ever burst
    Into that silent Sea.

Down dropt the breeze, the Sails dropt down,
    'Twas sad as sad could be
And we did speak only to break
    The silence of the Sea.

All in a hot and copper sky
    The bloody sun at noon,
Right up above the mast did stand,
    No bigger than the moon.

Day after day, day after day,
    We stuck, ne breath ne motion,
As idle as a painted Ship
    Upon a painted Ocean.

Water, water, every where
    And all the boards did shrink;
Water, water every where,
    Ne any drop to drink.

The very deeps did rot: O Christ!
  That ever this should be!
Yea, slimy things did crawl with legs
  Upon the slimy Sea.

SAMUEL TAYLOR COLERIDGE
from 'The Rime of the
Ancyent Marinere (1798)'

The Storm

Thou which art I, ('tis nothing to be so)
Thou which art still thyself, by these shalt know
Part of our passage; and, a hand, or eye
By Hilliard drawn, is worth an history,
By a worse painter made; and (without pride)
When by thy judgement they are dignified,
My lines are such: 'tis the pre-eminence
Of friendship only to impute excellence.
England to whom we owe, what we be, and have,
Sad that her sons did seek a foreign grave
(For, Fate's, or Fortune's drifts none can soothsay,
Honour and misery have one face and way)
From out her pregnant entrails sighed a wind
Which at th' air's middle marble room did find
Such strong resistance, that itself it threw
Downward again; and so when it did view
How in the port, our fleet dear time did leese,
Withering like prisoners, which lie but for fees,
Mildly it kissed our sails, and, fresh and sweet,
As to a stomach starved, whose insides meet,
Meat comes, it came; and swole our sails, when we
So joyed, as Sara her swelling joyed to see.

But 'twas but so kind, as our countrymen,
Which bring friends one day's way, and leave them then.
Then like two mighty kings, which dwelling far
Asunder, meet against a third to war,
The south and west winds joined, and, as they blew,
Waves like a rolling trench before them threw.
Sooner than you read this line, did the gale,
Like shot, not feared till felt, our sails assail;
And what at first was called a gust, the same
Hath now a storm's, anon a tempest's name.
Jonas, I pity thee, and curse those men,
Who when the storm raged most, did wake thee then;
Sleep is pain's easiest salve, and doth fulfil
All offices of death, except to kill.
But when I waked, I saw, that I saw not.
I, and the sun, which should teach me had forgot
East, west, day, night, and I could only say,
If the world had lasted, now it had been day.
Thousands our noises were, yet we 'mongst all
Could none by his right name, but thunder call:
Lightning was all our light, and it rained more
Than if the sun had drunk the sea before.
Some coffined in their cabins lie, equally
Grieved that they are not dead, and yet must die.
And as sin-burdened souls from graves will creep,
At the last day, some forth their cabins peep:
And tremblingly ask what news, and do hear so,
Like jealous husbands, what they would not know.
Some sitting on the hatches, would seem there,
With hideous gazing to fear away fear.
Then note they the ship's sicknesses, the mast
Shaked with this ague, and the hold and waist
With a salt dropsy clogged, and all our tacklings
Snapping, like too high stretched treble strings.

And from our tottered sails, rags drop down so,
As from one hanged in chains, a year ago.
Even our ordnance placed for our defence,
Strive to break loose, and 'scape away from thence.
Pumping hath tired our men, and what's the gain?
Seas into seas thrown, we suck in again;
Hearing hath deafed our sailors; and if they
Knew how to hear, there's none knows what to say.
Compared to these storms, death is but a qualm,
Hell somewhat lightsome, and the Bermuda calm.
Darkness, light's elder brother, his birth-right
Claims o'er this world, and to heaven hath chased light.
All things are one, and that one none can be,
Since all forms, uniform deformity
Doth cover, so that we, except God say
Another *Fiat*, shall have no more day.
So violent, yet long these furies be,
That though thine absence starve me, I wish not thee.

JOHN DONNE

The Calm

Our storm is past, and that storm's tyrannous rage,
A stupid calm, but nothing it, doth 'suage.
The fable is inverted, and far more
A block afflicts, now, than a stork before.
Storms chafe, and soon wear out themselves, or us;
In calms, heaven laughs to see us languish thus.
As steady as I can wish, that my thoughts were,
Smooth as thy mistress' glass, or what shines there,
The sea is now. And, as those Isles which we
Seek, when we can move, our ships rooted be.

As water did in storms, now pitch runs out
As lead, when a fired church becomes one spout.
And all our beauty, and our trim, decays,
Like courts removing, or like ended plays.
The fighting place now seamen's rags supply;
And all the tackling is a frippery.
No use of lanthorns; and in one place lay
Feathers and dust, today and yesterday.
Earth's hollownesses, which the world's lungs are,
Have no more wind than the upper vault of air.
We can nor lost friends, nor sought foes recover,
But meteor-like, save that we move not, hover.
Only the calenture together draws
Dear friends, which meet dead in great fishes' jaws:
And on the hatches as on altars lies
Each one, his own priest, and own sacrifice.
Who live, that miracle do multiply
Where walkers in hot ovens, do not die.
If in despite of these, we swim, that hath
No more refreshing, than our brimstone bath,
But from the sea, into the ship we turn,
Like parboiled wretches, on the coals to burn.
Like Bajazet encaged, the shepherd's scoff,
Or like slack-sinewed Samson, his hair off,
Languish our ships. Now, as a myriad
Of ants, durst th'Emperor's loved snake invade,
The crawling galleys, sea-gaols, finny chips,
Might brave our pinnaces, now bed-rid ships.
Whether a rotten state, and hope of gain,
Or, to disuse me from the queasy pain
Of being beloved, and loving, or the thirst
Of honour, or fair death, out pushed me first,
I lose my end: for here as well as I
A desperate may live, and a coward die.

Stag, dog, and all which from, or towards flies,
Is paid with life, or prey, or doing dies.
Fate grudges us all, and doth subtly lay
A scourge, 'gainst which we all forget to pray,
He that at sea prays for more wind, as well
Under the poles may beg cold, heat in hell.
What are we then? How little more alas
Is man now, than before he was! he was
Nothing; for us, we are for nothing fit;
Chance, or ourselves still disproportion it.
We have no power, no will, no sense; I lie,
I should not then thus feel this misery.

JOHN DONNE

In the Southern Ocean

January, 1828.   This day we found ourselves completely
hemmed in by the ice, and our prospects looked cheerless
indeed. A strong gale blew, during the whole forenoon, from
the northeast, and drove large cakes of the drift against the
rudder and counter with such violence that we all trembled for
the consequences. Towards evening, the gale still blowing with
fury, a large field in front separated, and we were enabled, by
carrying a press of sail, to force a passage through the smaller
flakes into some open water beyond. As we approached this
space we took in sail by degrees, and having at length got clear,
lay to under a single reefed foresail.

January 2.   We had now tolerably pleasant weather. At noon
we found ourselves in latitude 69° 10' S., longitude 42° 20' W.,
having crossed the Antarctic circle. Very little ice was to be seen
to the southward, although large fields of it lay behind us. This
day we rigged some sounding gear, using a large iron pot capable

of holding twenty gallons, and a line of two hundred fathoms. We found the current setting to the north, about a quarter of a mile per hour. The temperature of the air was now about thirty-three. Here we found the variation to be 14° 28' easterly, per azimuth.

January 5.   We had still held on to the southward without any very great impediments. On this morning, however, being in latitude 73° 15' S., longitude 42° 10' W., we were again brought to a stand by an immense expanse of firm ice. We saw, nevertheless, much open water to the southward, and felt no doubt of being able to reach it eventually. Standing to the eastward along the edge of the floe, we at length came to a passage of about a mile in width, through which we warped our way by sundown. The sea in which we now were was thickly covered with ice islands, but had no field ice, and we pushed on boldly as before. The cold did not seem to increase, although we had snow very frequently, and now and then hail squalls of great violence. Immense flocks of the albatross flew over the schooner this day, going from southeast to northwest.

January 7.   The sea still remained pretty well open, so that we had no difficulty in holding on our course. To the westward we saw some icebergs of incredible size, and in the afternoon passed very near one whose summit could not have been less than four hundred fathoms from the surface of the ocean. Its girth was probably, at the base, three quarters of a league, and several streams of water were running from crevices in its sides. We remained in sight of this island two days, and then only lost it in a fog.

January 10.   Early this morning we had the misfortune to lose a man overboard. He was an American, named Peter Vredenburgh, a native of New York, and was one of the most valuable hands on board the schooner. In going over the bows his foot slipped, and he fell between two cakes of ice, never rising again. At noon of this day we were in latitude 78° 30', longitude 40° 15' W. The cold was now excessive, and we had hail squalls continually from the northward and eastward. In this direction also we saw several more immense icebergs, and the whole horizon to the eastward appeared to be blocked up with field ice, rising in tiers, one mass above the other. Some driftwood floated by during the evening, and a great quantity of birds flew over, among which were nellies, petrels, albatrosses, and a large bird of a brilliant blue plumage. The variation here, per azimuth, was less than it had been previously to our passing the Antarctic circle.

January 12. Our passage to the south again looked doubtful, as nothing was to be seen in the direction of the pole but one apparently limitless floe, backed by absolute mountains of ragged ice, one precipice of which arose frowningly above the other. We stood to the westward until the fourteenth, in the hope of finding an entrance.

January 14. This morning we reached the western extremity of the field which had impeded us, and, weathering it, came to an open sea, without a particle of ice. Upon sounding with two hundred fathoms, we here found a current setting southwardly at the rate of half a mile per hour. The temperature of the air was forty-seven, that of the water thirty-four. We now sailed to the southward without meeting any interruption of moment until the sixteenth, when, at noon, we were in latitude 81° 21', longitude 42° W. We here again sounded, and found a current setting still southwardly, and at the rate of three quarters of a mile per hour. The variation per azimuth had diminished, and the temperature of the air was mild and pleasant, the thermometer being as high as fifty-one. At this period not a particle of ice was to be discovered. All hands on board now felt certain on attaining the pole.

January 17. This day was full of incident. Innumerable flights of birds flew over us from the southward, and several were shot from the deck; one of them, a species of pelican, proved to be excellent eating. About midday a small floe of ice was seen from the masthead off the larboard bow, and upon it there appeared to be some large animal. As the weather was good and nearly calm, Captain Guy ordered out two of the boats to see what it was. Dirk Peters and myself accompanied the mate in the larger boat. Upon coming up with the floe, we perceived that it was in possession of a gigantic creature of the race of the Arctic bear, but far exceeding in size the largest of these animals. Being well armed, we made no scruple of attacking it at once. Several shots were fired in quick succession, the most of which took effect, apparently in the head and body. Nothing discouraged, however, the monster threw himself from the ice, and swam, with open jaws, to the boat in which were Peters and myself. Owing to the confusion which ensued among us at this unexpected turn of the adventure, no person was ready immediately with a second shot, and the bear had actually succeeded in getting half his vast bulk across our gunwale, and seizing one of the men by the small of his back, before any efficient means were taken to repel him. In this extremity nothing but the promptness and agility of Peters saved us from destruction. Leaping upon the back of the huge beast, he plunged the blade of a knife behind the neck, reaching the spinal marrow at a blow. The brute tumbled into the sea lifeless, and without a struggle, rolling over Peters as he fell. The latter soon recovered himself, and a rope being thrown him, he secured the carcass before entering the boat. We then returned in triumph to the schooner, towing our trophy behind us. This bear, upon admeasurement, proved to be full fifteen feet in his greatest length. His wool was perfectly white, and very coarse, curling tightly. The eyes were of a blood red, and larger than those of the Arctic bear – the snout also more rounded, rather resembling the snout of the bulldog. The meat was tender, but excessively rank and fishy, although the men devoured it with avidity, and declared it excellent eating.

Scarcely had we got our prize alongside, when the man at the masthead gave the joyful shout of '*land on the starboard bow!*' All hands were now upon the alert, and, a breeze springing up very opportunely from the northward and eastward, we were soon close in with the coast. It proved to be a low rocky islet, of about a league in circumference, and altogether destitute of vegetation, if we except a species of prickly pear. In approaching it from the northward, a singular ledge of rock is seen projecting into the sea, and bearing a strong resemblance to corded bales of cotton. Around this ledge to the westward is a small bay, at the bottom of which our boats effected a convenient landing.

It did not take us long to explore every portion of the island, but, with one exception, we found nothing worthy of observation. In the southern extremity, we picked up near the shore, half buried in a pile of loose stones, a piece of wood, which seemed to have formed the prow of a canoe. There had been evidently some attempt at carving upon it, and Captain Guy fancied that he made out the figure of a tortoise, but the resemblance did not strike me very forcibly. Besides this prow, if such it were, we found no other token that any living creature had ever been here before. Around the coast we discovered occasional small floes of ice – but these were very few. The exact situation of this islet (to which Captain Guy gave the name of Bennet's Islet, in honor of his partner in the ownership of the schooner) is 82° 50' S. latitude, 42° 20' W. longitude.

We had now advanced to the southward more than eight degrees farther than any previous navigators, and the sea still lay perfectly open before us. We found, too, that the variation uniformly decreased as we proceeded, and, what was still more surprising, that the temperature of the air, and latterly of the water, became milder. The weather might even be called pleasant, and we had a steady but very gentle breeze always from some northern point of the compass. The sky was usually clear, with now and then a slight appearance of thin vapor in the

southern horizon – this, however, was invariably of brief dur-
ation. Two difficulties alone presented themselves to our view;
we were getting short of fuel, and symptoms of scurvy had
occurred among several of the crew. These considerations began
to impress upon Captain Guy the necessity of returning, and he
spoke of it frequently. For my own part, confident as I was of
soon arriving at land of some description upon the course we
were pursuing, and having every reason to believe, from present
appearances, that we should not find it the sterile soil met with
in the higher Arctic latitudes, I warmly pressed upon him the
expediency of persevering, at least for a few days longer, in the
direction we were now holding. So tempting an opportunity of
solving the great problem in regard to an Antarctic continent
had never yet been afforded to man, and I confess that I felt
myself bursting with indignation at the timid and ill-timed
suggestions of our commander. I believe, indeed, that what I
could not refrain from saying to him on this head had the effect
of inducing him to push on. While, therefore, I cannot but
lament the most unfortunate and bloody events which immediately arose from my advice, I must still be allowed to feel some
degree of gratification at having been instrumental, however
remotely, in opening to the eye of science one of the most
intensely exciting secrets which has ever engrossed its attention.

EDGAR ALLAN POE
from *The Narrative of Arthur Gordon Pym of Nantucket*

Voyage to Ishmaelia

THE ships which William had missed had been modern and
commodious and swift; not so the *Francmaçon* in which he was
eventually obliged to sail. She had been built at an earlier epoch
in the history of steam navigation and furnished in the style of

the day, for service among the high waves and icy winds of the North Atlantic. Late June in the Gulf of Suez was not her proper place or season. There was no space on her decks for long chairs; her cabins, devoid of fans, were aired only by tiny portholes, built to resist the buffeting of an angrier sea. The passengers sprawled listlessly on the crimson plush settees of the lounge. Carved mahogany panels shut them in; a heraldic ceiling hung threateningly overhead; light came to them, dimly, from behind the imitation windows of stained, armorial glass, and, blinding white, from the open door, whence too came the sounds of the winch, the smell of cargo and hot iron, the patter of bare feet and the hoarse, scolding voice of the second officer.

William sat in a hot, soft chair, a map of Ishmaelia open upon his knees, his eyes shut, his head lolling forwards on his chest, fast asleep, dreaming about his private school, now, he noted without surprise, peopled by Negroes and governed by his grandmother. An appalling brass percussion crashed and sang an inch or two from his ear. A soft voice said, 'Lunce pliss.' The Javanese with the gong proceeded on his apocalyptic mission, leaving William hot and wet, without appetite, very sorry to be awake.

The French colonial administrator, who had been nursing his two children in the next arm-chair to William's, rose briskly. It was the first time that day they had met face to face, so they shook hands and commented on the heat. Every morning, William found, it was necessary to shake hands with all the passengers.

'And madame?'

'She suffers. You are still studying the map of Ishmaelia . . .' They turned together and descended the staircase towards the dining saloon; the functionary leading a tottering child by either hand. '. . . It is a country of no interest.'

'No.'

'It is not rich at all. If it were rich it would already belong to England. Why do you wish to take it?'

'But I do not wish to.'

'There is no oil, there is no tin, no gold, no iron – positively none,' said the functionary, growing vexed at such unreasonable rapacity. 'What do you want with it?'

'I am going as a journalist.'

'Ah, well, to the journalist every country is rich.'

They were alone at their table. The functionary arranged his napkin about his open throat, tucked the lowest corner into his cummerbund and lifted a child on to either knee. It was always thus that he sat at meals, feeding them to repletion, to surfeit, alternately, from his own plate. He wiped his glass on the tablecloth, put ice into it, and filled it with the harsh, blue-red wine that was included free in the menu. The little girl took a deep draught. 'It is excellent for their stomachs,' he explained, refilling for his son.

There were three empty places at their table. The administrator's wife, the Captain's, and the Captain's wife's. The last two were on the bridge directing the discharge of cargo. The Captain led a life of somewhat blatant domesticity; half the boat deck was given up to his quarters, where a vast brass bedstead was visible through the portholes, and a variety of unseamanlike furniture. The Captain's wife had hedged off a little veranda for herself with pots of palm and strings of newly laundered under-clothes. Here she passed the day stitching, ironing, flopping in and out of the deck-house in heelless slippers, armed with a feather brush, often emerging in a dense aura of Asiatic perfume to dine in the saloon; a tiny, hairless dog capered about her feet. But in port she was always at her husband's side, exchanging civilities with the company's agents and the quarantine inspectors, and arranging, in a small way, for the transfer of contraband.

'Even supposing there is oil in Ishmaelia,' said the administrator, resuming the conversation which had occupied him ever since, on the first night of the voyage, William had disclosed his destination, 'how are you going to get it out?'

'But I have no interest in commerce. I am going to report the war.'

'War is all commerce.'

William's command of French, just adequate, inaccurately, for the exchange of general information and the bare courtesies of daily intercourse, was not strong enough for sustained argument, so now, as at every meal, he left the Frenchman victorious, saying '*Peut-être*,' with what he hoped was Gallic scepticism, and turning his attention to the dish beside him.

It was a great, white fish, cold and garnished; the children had rejected it with cries of distress; it lay on a charger of imitation silver; the two brown thumbs of the coloured steward lay just within the circle of mayonnaise; lozenges and roundels of coloured vegetable spread symmetrically about its glazed back. William looked sadly at this fish. 'It is very dangerous,' said the administrator. 'In the tropics one easily contrasts disease of the skin . . .'

EVELYN WAUGH
from *Scoop*

Castaway

The last of these voyages not proving very fortunate, I grew weary of the sea, and intended to stay at home with my wife and family. I removed from the Old Jury to Fetter Lane, and from thence to Wapping, hoping to get business among the sailors; but it would not turn to account. After three years' expectation that things would mend, I accepted an advantageous offer from Captain William Prichard, master of the *Antelope*, who was making a voyage to the South Sea. We set sail from Bristol, May 4th, 1699, and our voyage at first was very prosperous.

It would not be proper, for some reasons, to trouble the

reader with the particulars of our adventures in those seas: let it suffice to inform him, that in our passage from thence to the East Indies, we were driven by a violent storm to the north-west of Van Diemen's Land. By an observation, we found ourselves in the latitude of 30 degrees 2 minutes south. Twelve of our crew were dead by immoderate labour, and ill food, the rest were in a very weak condition. On the fifth of November, which was the beginning of summer in those parts, the weather being very hazy, the seamen spied a rock, within half a cable's length of the ship; but the wind was so strong, that we were driven directly upon it, and immediately split. Six of the crew, of whom I was one, having let down the boat into the sea, made a shift to get clear of the ship, and the rock. We rowed by my computation about three leagues, till we were able to work no longer, being already spent with labour while we were in the ship. We therefore trusted ourselves to the mercy of the waves, and in about half an hour the boat was overset by a sudden flurry from the north. What became of my companions in the boat, as well as of those who escaped on the rock, or were left in the vessel, I cannot tell; but conclude they were all lost. For my own part, I swam as Fortune directed me, and was pushed forward by wind and tide. I often let my legs drop, and could feel no bottom: but when I was almost gone, and able to struggle no longer, I found myself within my depth; and by this time the storm was much abated. The declivity was so small, that I walked near a mile before I got to the shore, which I conjectured was about eight o'clock in the evening. I then advanced forward near half a mile, but could not discover any sign of houses or inhabitants; at least I was in so weak a condition, that I did not observe them. I was extremely tired, and with that, and the heat of the weather, and about half a pint of brandy that I drank as I left the ship, I found myself much inclined to sleep. I lay down on the grass, which was very short and soft, where I slept sounder than ever I remember to have done in my life, and as I reckoned, above nine hours; for when I awaked, it was just daylight. I attempted to rise, but was not able to stir: for as I happened to lie on my back, I found my arms and legs were strongly fastened on each side to the ground; and my hair, which was long and thick, tied down in the same manner. I likewise felt several slender ligatures across my body, from my armpits to my thighs. I could only look upwards, the sun began to grow hot, and the light offended mine eyes. I heard a confused noise about me, but in the posture I lay, could see nothing except the sky. In a little time I felt something alive moving on my left leg, which advancing gently forward over my breast, came almost up to my chin; when bending mine eyes downwards as much as I could, I perceived it to be a human creature not six inches high, with a bow and arrow in his hands, and a quiver at his back . . .

JONATHAN SWIFT
from *Gulliver's Travels*

Henry I to the Sea

O Sea, take all, since thou hast taken him
 Whose life to me was life. Let one wide wave
 Now sweep this land, and make a single grave
For king and people. Let the wild gull skim

Where now is England, and the sea-fish swim
 In every drowned cathedral's vaulted nave,
 As in a green and pillared ocean cave,
Submerged for ever and for ever dim.

And if the shuddering pilot ventures there
  And sees their pinnacles, like rocks to shun,
Above the waves, and green with tidal hair,

Then let him whisper that this thing was done
  By God, the Lord of Oceans, at the prayer
Of England's king, who mourned his only son.

EUGENE LEE-HAMILTON

'I see huge dreadful Arctic and Antarctic icebergs'

I see huge dreadful Arctic and Antarctic icebergs,
I see the superior oceans and the inferior ones, the Atlantic
    and Pacific, the sea of Mexico, the Brazilian sea, and the
    sea of Peru,
The waters of Hindustan, the China sea, and the gulf of
    Guinea,
The Japan waters, the beautiful bay of Nagasaki land-lock'd
    in its mountains,
The spread of the Baltic, Caspian, Bothnia, the British shores,
    and the bay of Biscay,
The clear-sunn'd Mediterranean, and from one to another of
    its islands,
The White sea, and the sea around Greenland.

I behold the mariners of the world,
Some are in storms, some in the night with the watch on the
    lookout,
Some drifting helplessly, some with contagious diseases.

I behold the sail and steamships of the world, some in
    clusters in port, some on their voyages,
Some double the cape of Storms, some cape Verde, others
    capes Guardafui, Bon, or Bajadore,
Others Dondra head, others pass the straits of Sunda, others
    cape Lopatka, others Behring's straits,
Others cape Horn, others sail the gulf of Mexico or along
    Cuba or Hayti, others Hudson's bay or Baffin's bay,
Others pass the straits of Dover, others enter the Wash,
    others the firth of Solway, others round cape Clear,
    others the Land's End,
Others traverse the Zuyder Zee or the Scheld,
Others as comers and goers at Gibraltar or the Dardanelles,
Others sternly push their way through the northern
    winter-packs,
Others descend or ascend the Obi or the Lena,
Others the Niger or the Congo, others the Indus, the
    Burampooter and Cambodia,
Others wait steam'd up ready to start in the ports of
    Australia,
Wait at Liverpool, Glasgow, Dublin, Marseilles, Lisbon,
    Naples, Hamburg, Bremen, Bordeaux, the Hague,
    Copenhagen,
Wait at Valparaiso, Rio Janeiro, Panama.

WALT WHITMAN
from 'Salut au Monde!'

Rounding Cape Horn

DECEMBER 21ST – The *Beagle* got under way: and on the
succeeding day, favoured to an uncommon degree by a fine
easterly breeze, we closed in with the Barnevelts, and, running
past Cape Deceit with its stony peaks, about three o'clock

doubled the weatherbeaten Cape Horn. The evening was calm and bright, and we enjoyed a fine view of the surrounding isles. Cape Horn, however, demanded his tribute, and before night sent us a gale of wind directly in our teeth. We stood out to sea, and on the second day again made the land, when we saw on our weather-bow this notorious promontory in its proper form – veiled in a mist, and its dim outline surrounded by a storm of wind and water. Great black clouds were rolling across the heavens, and squalls of rain, with hail, swept by us with extreme violence so that the captain determined to run into Wigwam Cove. This is a snug little harbour, not far from Cape Horn; and here, at Christmas-eve, we anchored in smooth water. The only thing which reminded us of the gale outside, was every now and then a puff from the mountains, which seemed to wish to blow us out of the water.

CHARLES DARWIN
from *Voyage of the* Beagle

Rounding Cape Horn

Sunday, Nov. 9th. To-day the sun rose clear, and continued so until twelve o'clock, when the captain got an observation. This was very well for Cape Horn, and we thought it a little remarkable that, as we had not had one unpleasant Sunday during the whole voyage, the only tolerable day here should be a Sunday. We got time to clear up the steerage and forecastle, and set things to rights, and to overhaul our wet clothes a little. But this did not last very long. Between five and six – the sun was then nearly three hours high – the cry of 'All starbowlines ahoy!' summoned our watch on deck; and immediately all hands were called. A true specimen of Cape Horn was coming upon us. A great cloud of a dark slate-color was driving on us from the south-west; and we did our best to take in sail, (for the light sails had been

set during the first part of the day,) before we were in the midst
of it. We had got the light sails furled, the courses hauled up,
and the topsail reef-tackles hauled out, and were just mounting
the fore-rigging, when the storm struck us. In an instant the
sea, which had been comparatively quiet, was running higher
and higher; and it became almost as dark as night. The hail and
sleet were harder than I had yet felt them; seeming almost to
pin us down to the rigging. We were longer taking in sail than
ever before; for the sails were stiff and wet, the ropes and rigging
covered with snow and sleet, and we ourselves cold and nearly
blinded with the violence of the storm. By the time we had got
down upon deck again, the little brig was plunging madly into
a tremendous head sea, which at every drive rushed in through
the bow-ports and over the bows, and buried all the forward
part of the vessel. At this instant the chief mate, who was
standing on the top of the windlass, at the foot of the spenser
mast, called out, 'Lay out there and furl the jib!' This was no
agreeable or safe duty, yet it must be done. An old Swede, (the
best sailor on board,) who belonged on the forecastle, sprang
out upon the bowsprit. Another one must go: I was near the mate,
and sprang forward, threw the downhaul over the windlass, and
jumped between the knight-heads out upon the bowsprit. The
crew stood abaft the windlass and hauled the jib down, while
we got out upon the weather side of the jib-boom, our feet on
the foot-ropes, holding on by the spar, the great jib flying off
to leeward and *slatting* so as almost to throw us off of the boom.
For some time we could do nothing but hold on, and the vessel
diving into two huge seas, one after the other, plunged us twice
into the water up to our chins. We hardly knew whether we
were on or off; when coming up, dripping from the water, we
were raised high into the air. John (that was the sailor's name)
thought the boom would go, every moment, and called out to
the mate to keep the vessel off, and haul down the staysail; but
the fury of the wind and the breaking of the seas against the

bows defied every attempt to make ourselves heard, and we were obliged to do the best we could in our situation. Fortunately, no other seas so heavy struck her, and we succeeded in furling the jib 'after a fashion;' and, coming in over the staysail nettings, were not a little pleased to find that all was snug, and the watch gone below; for we were soaked through, and it was very cold. The weather continued nearly the same through the night.

RICHARD HENRY DANA, JR.
from *Two Years before the Mast*

A Narrow Escape

It was the larboard watch's turn to remain below from midnight till four o'clock; and having turned in and slept, Blunt suddenly turned out again about three o'clock, with a wonderful dream in his head; which he was desirous of at once having interpreted.

So he goes to his chest, gets out his tools, and falls to ciphering on the lid. When, all at once, a terrible cry was heard, that routed him and all the rest of us up, and sent the whole ship's company flying on deck in the dark. We did not know what it was; but somehow, among sailors at sea, they seem to know when real danger of any kind is at hand, even in their sleep.

When we got on deck, we saw the mate standing on the bowsprit, and crying out *Luff! Luff!* to some one in the dark water before the ship. In that direction, we could just see a light, and then, the great black hull of a strange vessel, that was coming down on us obliquely; and so near, that we heard the flap of her topsails as they shook in the wind, the trampling of feet on the deck, and the same cry of *Luff! Luff!* that our own mate was raising.

In a minute more, I caught my breath, as I heard a snap and

a crash, like the fall of a tree, and suddenly, one of our flying-jib guys jerked out the bolt near the cat-head; and presently, we heard our jib-boom thumping against our bows.

Meantime, the strange ship, scraping by us thus, shot off into the darkness, and we saw her no more. But she, also, must have been injured; for when it grew light, we found pieces of strange rigging mixed with ours. We repaired the damage, and replaced the broken spar with another jib-boom we had; for all ships carry spare spars against emergencies.

The cause of this accident, which came near being the death of all on board, was nothing but the drowsiness of the look-out men on the forecastles of both ships. The sailor who had the look-out on our vessel was terribly reprimanded by the mate.

No doubt, many ships that are never heard of after leaving port, meet their fate in this way; and it may be, that sometimes two vessels coming together, jib-boom-and-jib-boom, with a sudden shock in the middle watch of the night, mutually destroy each other; and like fighting elks, sink down into the ocean, with their antlers locked in death.

While I was at Liverpool, a fine ship that lay near us in the docks, having got her cargo on board, went to sea, bound for India, with a good breeze; and all her crew felt sure of a prosperous voyage. But in about seven days after, she came back, a most distressing object to behold. All her starboard side was torn and splintered; her starboard anchor was gone; and a great part of the starboard bulwarks; while every one of the lower yard-arms had been broken, in the same direction; so that she now carried small and unsightly *jury-yards*.

When I looked at this vessel, with the whole of one side thus shattered, but the other still in fine trim; and when I remembered her gay and gallant appearance, when she left the same harbor into which she now entered so forlorn; I could not help thinking of a young man I had known at home, who had left his cottage one morning in high spirits, and was brought back at noon with his right side paralyzed from head to foot.

It seems that this vessel had been run against by a strange ship, crowding all sail before a fresh breeze; and the stranger had rushed past her starboard side, reducing her to the sad state in which she now was.

Sailors can not be too wakeful and cautious, when keeping their night look-outs; though, as I well know, they too often suffer themselves to become negligent, and nod. And this is not so wonderful, after all; for though every seaman has heard of those accidents at sea; and many of them, perhaps, have been in ships that have suffered from them; yet, when you find yourself sailing along on the ocean at night, without having seen a sail for weeks and weeks, it is hard for you to realize that any are near. Then, if they *are* near, it seems almost incredible that on the broad, boundless sea, which washes Greenland at one end of the world, and the Falkland Islands at the other, that any one vessel upon such a vast highway, should come into close contact with another. But the likelihood of great calamities occurring, seldom obtrudes upon the minds of ignorant men, such as sailors generally are; for the things which wise people know, anticipate, and guard against, the ignorant can only become acquainted with, by meeting them face to face. And even when experience has taught them, the lesson only serves for that day; inasmuch as the foolish in prosperity are infidels to the possibility of adversity; they see the sun in heaven, and believe it to be far too bright ever to set.

And even, as suddenly as the bravest and fleetest ships, while careering in pride of canvas over the sea, have been struck, as by lightning, and quenched out of sight; even so, do some lordly men, with all their plans and prospects gallantly trimmed to the fair, rushing breeze of life, and with no thought of death and disaster, suddenly encounter a shock unforeseen, and go down, foundering, into death.

HERMAN MELVILLE
from *Redburn*

from *An Humble Wish. Off Porto-Santo, March 29, 1779*

I've served my country nine and twenty years,
A mere light chip, the sport of all the spheres:
To India I was early sent in youth;
Then bandied to the north, the west, and south;
France, Holland, Prussia, Portugal, and Spain,
America, and all the western main.
Now I'm for Guinea, in an infant war,
Chief of a gallant ship, where ev'ry tar,
Ragged and lousy, hungry is and poor,
Well fitted a rich Frenchman to devour.
As for sea hardships, they create my smiles –
We'll bury them in the Canary Isles,
In the soft lap of beauteous Portuguese,
The olive Sirens of those summer seas.
Now for my wish – and Venus hear the strain!
When I've this bark conducted o'er the main,
And I return with golden laurels bound,
Parcel me out a little fertile ground,
And build thereon a house, by some thick wood,
And at the mountain's foot a rapid flood:
The river stored with trout, the wood with game,
And lovely Emma my propitious dame!
Retired from war, the bustle of the seas,
Let me repose with her in health and ease;

I seek no star or honours of the land;
I'd rather have a kiss of her white hand
Than all the salutations of St. James,
Where nobles truck their characters for names.
I only bend my knee to her and heaven,
Nor pray for aught, but thank for what is given.
If ye who rule the clouds, and guide the sun,
Will perfect this before my sand is run,
I bow – if not, your mighty wills be done.

EDWARD THOMPSON

Ulysses

It little profits that an idle king,
By this still hearth, among these barren crags,
Match'd with an agèd wife, I mete and dole
Unequal laws unto a savage race,
That hoard, and sleep, and feed, and know not me.

I cannot rest from travel: I will drink
Life to the lees: all times I have enjoy'd
Greatly, have suffer'd greatly, both with those
That loved me, and alone; on shore, and when
Thro' scudding drifts the rainy Hyades
Vext the dim sea: I am become a name;
For always roaming with a hungry heart
Much have I seen and known; cities of men
And manners, climates, councils, governments,
Myself not least, but honour'd of them all;
And drunk delight of battle with my peers,
Far on the ringing plains of windy Troy.
I am a part of all that I have met;

Yet all experience is an arch wherethro'
Gleams that untravell'd world, whose margin fades,
For ever and for ever when I move.
How dull it is to pause, to make an end,
To rust unburnish'd, not to shine in use!
As tho' to breathe were life. Life piled on life
Were all too little, and of one to me
Little remains: but every hour is saved
From that eternal silence, something more,
A bringer of new things; and vile it were
For some three suns to store and hoard myself,
And this gray spirit yearning in desire
To follow knowledge like a sinking star,
Beyond the utmost bound of human thought.

This is my son, mine own Telemachus,
To whom I leave the sceptre and the isle –
Well-loved of me, discerning to fulfil
This labour, by slow prudence to make mild
A rugged people, and thro' soft degrees
Subdue them to the useful and the good.
Most blameless is he, centred in the sphere
Of common duties, decent not to fail
In offices of tenderness, and pay
Meet adoration to my household gods,
When I am gone. He works his work, I mine.

There lies the port; the vessel puffs her sail:
There gloom the dark broad seas. My mariners,
Souls that have toil'd, and wrought, and thought with me –
That ever with a frolic welcome took
The thunder and the sunshine, and opposed
Free hearts, free foreheads – you and I are old;
Old age hath yet his honour and his toil;

Death closes all: but something ere the end,
Some work of noble note, may yet be done,
Not unbecoming men that strove with Gods.
The lights begin to twinkle from the rocks:
The long day wanes: the slow moon climbs: the deep
Moans round with many voices. Come, my friends,
'Tis not too late to seek a newer world.
Push off, and sitting well in order smite
The sounding furrows; for my purpose holds
To sail beyond the sunset, and the baths
Of all the western stars, until I die.
It may be that the gulfs will wash us down:
It may be we shall touch the Happy Isles,
And see the great Achilles, whom we knew.
Tho' much is taken, much abides; and tho'
We are not now that strength which in old days
Moved earth and heaven; that which we are, we are;
One equal temper of heroic hearts,
Made weak by time and fate, but strong in will
To strive, to seek, to find, and not to yield.

ALFRED LORD TENNYSON

The Shipman

A SHIPMAN was ther, wonynge fer by weste;
For aught I woot, he was of Dertemouthe.
He rood upon a rouncy, as he kouthe,
In a gowne of faldyng to the knee.
A daggere hangynge on a laas hadde he
Aboute his nekke, under his arm adoun.
The hoote somer hadde maad his hewe al broun;
And certeinly he was a good felawe.

Ful many a draughte of wyn had he ydrawe
Fro Burdeux-ward, whil that the chapman sleep.
Of nyce conscience took he no keep.
If that he faught and hadde the hyer hond,
By water he sente hem hoom to every lond.
But of his craft to rekene wel his tydes,
His stremes, and his daungers hym bisides,
His herberwe, and his moone, his lodemenage,
Ther nas noon swich from Hulle to Cartage.
Hardy he was and wys to undertake;
With many a tempest hadde his berd been shake.
He knew alle the havenes, as they were,
Fro Gootlond to the cape of Fynystere,
And every cryke in Britaigne and in Spayne.
His barge ycleped was the Maudelayne.

GEOFFREY CHAUCER
from 'The General Prologue'

A Typhoon in the South China Sea

JUKES was as ready a man as any half-dozen young mates that may be caught by casting a net upon the waters; and though he had been somewhat taken aback by the startling viciousness of the first squall, he had pulled himself together on the instant, had called out the hands and had rushed them along to secure such openings about the deck as had not been already battened down earlier in the evening. Shouting in his fresh, stentorian voice, 'Jump, boys, and bear a hand!' he led in the work, telling himself the while that he had 'just expected this'.

But at the same time he was growing aware that this was rather more than he had expected. From the first stir of the air felt on his cheek the gale seemed to take upon itself the accumulated impetus of an avalanche. Heavy sprays enveloped the *Nan-Shan* from stem to stern, and instantly in the midst of her regular rolling she began to jerk and plunge as though she had gone mad with fright.

Jukes thought, 'This is no joke.' While he was exchanging explanatory yells with his captain, a sudden lowering of the darkness came upon the night, falling before their vision like something palpable. It was as if the masked lights of the world had been turned down. Jukes was uncritically glad to have his captain at hand. It relieved him as though that man had, by simply coming on deck, taken most of the gale's weight upon his shoulders. Such is the prestige, the privilege, and the burden of command.

Captain MacWhirr could expect no relief of that sort from any one on earth. Such is the loneliness of command. He was trying to see, with that watchful manner of a seaman who stares into the wind's eye as if into the eye of an adversary, to penetrate the hidden intention and guess the aim and force of the thrust. The strong wind swept at him out of a vast obscurity; he felt under his feet the uneasiness of his ship, and he could not even discern the shadow of her shape. He wished it were not so; and very still he waited, feeling stricken by a blind man's helplessness.

To be silent was natural to him, dark or shine. Jukes, at his elbow, made himself heard yelling cheerily in the gusts, 'We must have got the worst of it at once, sir.' A faint burst of lightning quivered all round, as if flashed into a cavern – into a black and secret chamber of the sea, with a floor of foaming crests.

It unveiled for a sinister, fluttering moment a ragged mass of clouds hanging low, the lurch of the long outlines of the ship, the black figures of men caught on the bridge, heads forward, as if petrified in the act of butting. The darkness palpitated down upon all this, and then the real thing came at last.

It was something formidable and swift, like the sudden

smashing of a vial of wrath. It seemed to explode all round the ship with an overpowering concussion and rush of great waters, as if an immense dam had been blown up to windward. In an instant the men lost touch of each other. This is the disintegrating power of a great wind: it isolates one from one's kind. An earthquake, a landslip, an avalanche, overtake a man incidentally, as it were – without passion. A furious gale attacks him like a personal enemy, tries to grasp his limbs, fastens upon his mind, seeks to rout his very spirit out of him.

Jukes was driven away from his commander. He fancied himself whirled a great distance through the air. Everything disappeared – even, for a moment, his power of thinking; but his hand had found one of the rail-stanchions. His distress was by no means alleviated by an inclination to disbelieve the reality of this experience. Though young, he had seen some bad weather, and had never doubted his ability to imagine the worst; but this was so much beyond his powers of fancy that it appeared incompatible with the existence of any ship whatever. He would have been incredulous about himself in the same way, perhaps, had he not been so harassed by the necessity of exerting a wrestling effort against a force trying to tear him away from his hold. Moreover, the conviction of not being utterly destroyed returned to him through the sensations of being half-drowned, bestially shaken, and partly choked.

It seemed to him he remained there precariously alone with the stanchion for a long, long time. The rain poured on him, flowed, drove in sheets. He breathed in gasps; and sometimes the water he swallowed was fresh and sometimes it was salt. For the most part he kept his eyes shut tight, as if suspecting his sight might be destroyed in the immense flurry of the elements. When he ventured to blink hastily, he derived some moral support from the green gleam of the starboard light shining feebly upon the flight of rain and sprays. He was actually looking at it when its ray fell upon the uprearing sea which put it out.

He saw the head of the wave topple over, adding the mite of its crash to the tremendous uproar raging around him, and almost at the same instant the stanchion was wrenched away from his embracing arms. After a crushing thump on his back he found himself suddenly afloat and borne upwards. His first irresistible notion was that the whole China Sea had climbed on the bridge. Then, more sanely, he concluded himself gone overboard. All the time he was being tossed, flung, and rolled in great volumes of water, he kept on repeating mentally, with the utmost precipitation, the words: 'My God! My God! My God! My God!'

JOSEPH CONRAD
from *Typhoon*

The North-west Passage Proven

Four famous ways there be spoken of to those fruitful and wealthy islands, which we do usually call Moluccas, continually haunted for gain, and daily travelled for riches therein growing. These islands stand east from the meridian, distant almost half the length of the world, in extreme heat, under the equinoctial line, possessed of infidels and barbarians: yet great abundance of wealth there is painfully sought in respect of the voyage dearly bought, and from thence dangerously brought home. The Portuguese voyage is very well understood of all men, and the southeastern way round about Africa by the Cape of Good Hope more spoken of, better known and travelled, than it may seem needful to discourse thereof.

The second way lieth southwest, between the West Indies or South America, and the south continent, through that narrow strait where Magellan first passed these latter years, leaving thereunto his name. The way no doubt the Spaniards would commodiously take, for that it lieth near unto their dominions there, could the current and winds as easily suffer them to return: for the which impossibility of striving against the force both of wind and stream, this passage is little or nothing used, although it be very well known.

The third way by the northeast, beyond all Europe and Asia, that worthy and renowned knight Sir Hugh Willoughby sought to his peril, enforced there to end his life for cold, congealed and frozen to death. And truly this consisteth rather in the imagination of geographers, than allowable either in reason, or approved by experience, as well it may appear by the unlikely sailing in that northern sea always clad with ice and snow, the foul mists and dark fogs in the cold climate, the little power of the sun to clear the air, the uncomfortable nights so near the Pole, five months long.

A fourth way to go unto these aforesaid happy islands Molucca Sir Humphrey Gilbert a learned and valiant knight discourseth at large. But the way is dangerous, the passage doubtful, the voyage not thoroughly known.

First, who can assure us of any passage rather by the north west, than by the north east? Do not both ways lie in equal distances from the North Pole? Is not the ocean sea beyond America farther distant from our meridian by 30 or 40 degrees west, than the extreme points of Cathay eastward, if Ortelius' general card of the world be true? In the northeast that noble knight Sir Hugh Willoughby perished for cold: and can you then promise a passenger any better hap by the northwest?

Grant the West Indies not to continue continent unto the Pole, grant there be a passage between these two lands, let the gulf lie nearer us than commonly in cards we find it set. Let the way be void of all difficulties, yet doth it not follow that we have free passage to Cathay. For example's sake: in the Mediterranean sea, we sail to Alexandria in Egypt, the barbarians bring their pearls and spices from the Moluccas up the Red Sea or Arabian gulf to Suez, scarcely three days journey from the aforesaid haven: yet have we no way by sea from Alexandria to the Moluccas, for that isthmus or little strait of land between the two seas. In like manner although the northern passage be free at 61 degrees of latitude, and the west ocean beyond America, usually called Mar del Sur, known to be open at 40 degrees elevation from the island Japan, yet three hundred leagues northerly above Japan: yet may there be land to hinder the through passage that way by sea, America there being joined together in one continent.

Furthermore it were to small purpose to make so long, so painful, so doubtful a voyage by such a new found way, if in Cathay you should neither be suffered to land for silks and silver, nor able to fetch the Molucca spices and pearl for piracy in those seas.

Finally, all this great labour would be lost, all these charges spent in vain, if in the end our travellers might not be able to return again, and bring safely home into their own native country that wealth and riches, which they in foreign regions with adventure of goods, and danger of their lives have sought for. By the northeast there is no way, the southeast passage the Portuguese do hold as the lords of those seas. At the southwest Magellan's experience hath taught us the eastern current striketh so furiously on that strait, and falleth with such force into that narrow gulf, that hardly any ship can return that way.

To answer the objection, besides Cabot and all other travellers' navigations, the only credit of Mr Frobisher may suffice, who lately through all these islands of ice and mountains of snow, passed that way, even beyond the gulf that tumbleth down from the north, and in some places though he drew one inch thick ice, as he returning in August did, yet came he safely home again.

Whence I pray you came the contrary tide, that Mr Frobisher met withall after that he had sailed no small way in that passage, if there be any isthmus or strait of land betwixt the aforesaid northwestern gulf, and Mar del Sur, to join Asia and America together?

The rude Indian canoe hauleth those seas, the Portuguese, the Saracens, and Moors travel continually up and down that reach from Japan to China, from China to Malacca, from Malacca to the Moluccas: and shall an Englishman, better appointed than any of them all (that I say no more of our navy) fear to sail in that ocean? What seas at all do want piracy? What navigation is there void of peril?

Our travellers need not to seek their return by the northeast, neither shall they be constrained, except they list, either to attempt Magellan's strait at the southwest, or to be in danger of the Portuguese for the southeast: they may return by the northwest, that same way they do go forth.

RICHARD HAKLUYT
from *Voyages and Discoveries*

Stanzas from Carnac

Far on its rocky knoll descried
Saint Michael's chapel cuts the sky.
I climb'd; – beneath me, bright and wide,
Lay the lone coast of Brittany.

Bright in the sunset, weird and still,
It lay beside the Atlantic wave,
As though the wizard Merlin's will
Yet charm'd it from his forest-grave.

Behind me on their grassy sweep,
Bearded with lichen, scrawl'd and grey,
The giant stones of Carnac sleep,
In the mild evening of the May.

No priestly stern procession now
Moves through their rows of pillars old;
No victims bleed, no Druids bow –
Sheep make the daisied aisles their fold.

From bush to bush the cuckoo flies,
The orchis red gleams everywhere;
Gold furze with broom in blossom vies,
The blue-bells perfume all the air.

And o'er the glistening, lonely land,
Rise up, all round, the Christian spires;
The church of Carnac, by the strand,
Catches the westering sun's last fires.

And there, across the watery way,
See, low above the tide at flood,
The sickle-sweep of Quiberon Bay,
Whose beach once ran with loyal blood!

And beyond that, the Atlantic wide! –
All round, no soul, no boat, no hail;
But, on the horizon's verge descried,
Hangs, touch'd with light, one snowy sail!

Ah! where is he, who should have come
Where that far sail is passing now,
Past the Loire's mouth, and by the foam
Of Finistère's unquiet brow,

Home, round into the English wave?
– He tarries where the Rock of Spain
Mediterranean waters lave;
He enters not the Atlantic main.

Oh, could he once have reach'd this air
Freshen'd by plunging tides, by showers!
Have felt this breath he loved, of fair
Cool northern fields, and grass, and flowers!

He long'd for it – press'd on. – In vain!
At the Straits fail'd that spirit brave.
The south was parent of his pain,
The south is mistress of his grave.

MATTHEW ARNOLD

Floating Organisms

I will here add a few other observations connected with the discoloration of the sea from organic causes. On the coast of Chile, a few leagues north of Concepción, the *Beagle* one day passed through great bands of muddy water; and again, a degree south of Valparaiso, the same appearance was still more extensive. Although we were nearly 50 miles from the coast, I at first attributed this circumstance to real streams of muddy water brought down by the river Maypo. Mr Sulivan, however, having drawn up some in a glass, thought he distinguished, by the aid of a lens, moving points. The water was slightly stained as if by red dust; and after leaving it for some time quiet, a cloud collected at the bottom. With a lens, of one-fourth of an inch focal distance, small hyaline points could be seen darting about with great rapidity, and frequently exploding. Examined with a much higher power, their shape was found to be oval, and contracted by a ring round the middle, from which line curved little setæ proceeded on all sides; and these were the organs of motion. One end of the body was narrower and more pointed than the other. According to the arrangement of Bory St Vincent, they are animalcula, belonging to the family of Trichodes: it was, however, very difficult to examine them with care, for almost the instant motion ceased, even while crossing the field of vision, their bodies burst. Sometimes both ends burst at once, sometimes only one, and a quantity of coarse brownish granular matter was ejected, which cohered very slightly. The ring with the setæ sometimes retained its irritability for a little while after the contents of the body had been emptied, and continued a riggling, uneven motion. The animal an instant before bursting expanded to half again its natural size; and the explosion took place about fifteen seconds after the rapid progressive motion had ceased: in a few cases it was preceded for a short interval by a rotatory movement on the longer axis. About two minutes after any number were isolated in a drop of water, they thus perished. The animals move with the narrow apex forwards, by the aid of their vibratory ciliæ, and generally by rapid starts. They are exceedingly minute, and quite invisible to the naked eye, only covering a space equal to the square of the thousandth of an inch. Their numbers were infinite; for the smallest drop of water which I could remove contained very many. In one day we passed through two spaces of water thus stained, one of which alone must have extended over several square miles. What incalculable numbers of these microscopical animals! The colour of the water, as seen at some distance, was like that of a river which has flowed through a red clay district; but under the shade of the vessel's side, it was quite as dark as chocolate. The line where the red and blue water joined was distinctly defined. The weather for some days previously had been calm, and the ocean abounded, to an unusual degree, with living creatures. In Ulloa's *Voyage* an account is given of crossing, in nearly the same latitude, some discoloured water, which was mistaken for a shoal: no soundings were obtained, and I have no doubt, from the description, that this little animalcule was the cause of the alarm.

In the sea around Tierra del Fuego, and at no great distance from the land, I have seen narrow lines of water of a bright red colour, from the number of crustacea, which somewhat resemble in form large prawns. The sealers call them whale-food. Whether whales feed on them I do not know; but terns, cormorants, and immense herds of great unwieldly seals, on some parts of the coast, derive their chief sustenance from these swimming crabs. Seamen invariably attribute the discoloration of the water to spawn; but I found this to be the case only on one occasion. At the distance of several leagues from the Archipelago of the Galapagos, the ship sailed through three strips of a dark yellow-ish, or mud-like, water; these strips were some miles long, but only a few yards wide, and they were separated from the surrounding surface by a sinuous yet distinct margin. The colour was caused by little gelatinous balls, about the fifth of an inch in diameter, in which numerous minute spherical ovules were embedded: they were of two distinct kinds, one being of a reddish colour and of a different shape from the other. I cannot form a conjecture as to what two kinds of animals these belonged. Captain Colnett remarks, that this appearance is very common among the Galapagos Islands, and that the direction of the bands indicates that of the currents; in the described case, however, the line was caused by the wind. The only other appearance which I have to notice, is a thin oily coat on the surface which displays iridescent colours. I saw a considerable tract of the ocean thus covered on the coast of Brazil; the seamen attributed it to the putrefying carcass of some whale, which probably was floating at no great distance. I do not here mention the minute gelatinous particles which are frequently dispersed throughout the water, for they are not sufficiently abundant to create any change of colour.

There are two circumstances in the above accounts which appear very remarkable: first, how do the various bodies which form the bands with defined edges keep together? In the case of the prawn-like crabs, their movements were as co-instantaneous as in a regiment of soldiers; but this cannot happen from any thing like voluntary action with the ovules, or the confervæ, nor is it probable among the infusoria. Secondly, what causes the length and narrowness of the bands? The appearance so much resembles that which may be seen in every torrent, where the stream uncoils into long streaks, the froth collected in the eddies, that I must attribute the effect to a similar action either of the currents of the air, or sea. Under this supposition we must believe that the various organized bodies are produced in certain favourable places, and are thence removed by the set of either wind or water. I confess, however, there is a very great difficulty in imagining any one spot to be the birthplace of the millions of millions of animalcula and confervæ: for whence come the germs at such points? – the parent bodies having been distributed by the winds and waves over the immense ocean. But on no other hypothesis can I understand their linear grouping. I may add that Scoresby remarks, that green water abounding with pelagic animals, is invariably found in a certain part of the Arctic Sea.

CHARLES DARWIN
from *Voyage of the* Beagle

'In sooth I know not why I am so sad'

ANTONIO
　In sooth I knot not why I am so sad.
　It wearies me, you say it wearies you;
　But how I caught it, found it, or came by it,
　What stuff 'tis made of, whereof it is born,
　I am to learn;
　And such a want-wit sadness makes of me
　That I have much ado to know myself.

SALERIO
　Your mind is tossing on the ocean,
　There where your argosies with portly sail,
　Like signors and rich burghers on the flood,
　Or as it were the pageants of the sea,
　Do overpeer the pretty traffickers
　That curtsy to them, do them reverence,
　As they fly by them with their woven wings.

SOLANIO
　Believe me, sir, had I such venture forth,
　The better part of my affections would
　Be with my hopes abroad. I should be still
　Plucking the grass to know where sits the wind,
　Peering in maps for ports and piers and roads,
　And every object that might make me fear
　Misfortune to my ventures, out of doubt
　Would make me sad.

SALERIO　　　　　　　My wind cooling my broth
　Would blow me to an ague when I thought
　What harm a wind too great might do at sea.

I should not see the sandy hour-glass run
But I should think of shallows and of flats,
And see my wealthy Andrew docked in sand,
Vailing her high-top lower than her ribs
To kiss her burial. Should I go to church
And see the holy edifice of stone
And not bethink me straight of dangerous rocks,
Which touching but my gentle vessel's side
Would scatter all her spices on the stream,
Enrobe the roaring waters with my silks,
And in a word, but even now worth this,
And now worth nothing? Shall I have the thought
To think on this, and shall I lack the thought
That such a thing bechanced would make me sad?

WILLIAM SHAKESPEARE
from *The Merchant of Venice*, I, 1

The Buoy-Bell

How like the leper, with his own sad cry
Enforcing his own solitude, it tolls!
That lonely bell set in the rushing shoals,
To warn us from the place of jeopardy!
O friend of man! sore-vext by ocean's power,
The changing tides wash o'er thee day by day;
Thy trembling mouth is fill'd with bitter spray,
Yet still thou ringest on from hour to hour;
High is thy mission, though thy lot is wild –
To be in danger's realm a guardian sound;
In seamen's dreams a pleasant part to bear,

And earn their blessing as the year goes round;
And strike the key-note of each grateful prayer,
Breathed in their distant homes by wife or child!

CHARLES TENNYSON TURNER

The Convergence of the Twain
(Lines on the loss of the 'Titanic')

I

In a solitude of the sea
Deep from human vanity,
And the Pride of Life that planned her, stilly couches she.

II

Steel chambers, late the pyres
Of her salamandrine fires,
Cold currents thrid, and turn to rhythmic tidal lyres.

III

Over the mirrors meant
To glass the opulent
The sea-worm crawls – grotesque, slimed, dumb, indifferent.

IV

Jewels in joy designed
To ravish the sensuous mind
Lie lightless, all their sparkles bleared and black and blind.

V

Dim moon-eyed fishes near
Gaze at the gilded gear
And query: 'What does this vaingloriousness down here?' . . .

VI

Well: while was fashioning
This creature of cleaving wing,
The Immanent Will that stirs and urges everything

VII

Prepared a sinister mate
For her – so gaily great –
A Shape of Ice, for the time far and dissociate.

VIII

And as the smart ship grew
In stature, grace, and hue,
In shadowy silent distance grew the Iceberg too.

IX

Alien they seemed to be:
No mortal eye could see
The intimate welding of their later history,

X

Or a sign that they were bent
By paths coincident
On being anon twin halves of one august event,

XI

Till the Spinner of the Years
Said 'Now!' And each one hears,
And consummation comes, and jars two hemispheres.

THOMAS HARDY

Crossing the Bar

Sunset and evening star,
   And one clear call for me!
And may there be no moaning of the bar,
   When I put out to sea,

But such a tide as moving seems asleep,
   Too full for sound and foam,
When that which drew from out the boundless deep
   Turns again home.

Twilight and evening bell,
   And after that the dark!
And may there be no sadness of farewell,
   When I embark;

From tho' from out our bourne of Time and Place
   The flood may bear me far,
I hope to see my Pilot face to face
   When I have crost the bar.

ALFRED LORD TENNYSON

The Maldive Shark

About the Shark, phlegmatical one,
Pale sot of the Maldive sea,
The sleek little pilot-fish, azure and slim,
How alert in attendance be.

From his saw-pit of mouth, from his charnel of maw
They have nothing of harm to dread,
But liquidly glide on his ghastly flank
Or before his Gorgonian head;
Or lurk in the port of serrated teeth
In white triple tiers of glittering gates,
And there find a haven when peril's abroad,
An asylum in jaws of the Fates!
They are friends; and friendly they guide him to prey,
Yet never partake of the treat –
Eyes and brains to the dotard lethargic and dull,
Pale ravener of horrible meat.

HERMAN MELVILLE

The Kraken

Below the thunders of the upper deep;
Far, far beneath in the abysmal sea,
His ancient, dreamless, uninvaded sleep
The Kraken sleepeth: faintest sunlights flee
About his shadowy sides: above him swell
Huge sponges of millennial growth and height;
And far away into the sickly light,
From many a wondrous grot and secret cell
Unnumber'd and enormous polypi
Winnow with giant arms the slumbering green.

There hath he lain for ages and will lie
Battening upon huge seaworms in his sleep,
Until the latter fire shall heat the deep;
Then once by man and angels to be seen,
In roaring he shall rise and on the surface die.

ALFRED LORD TENNYSON

Verses, Supposed to be Written
by Alexander Selkirk
During his solitary abode in the
island of Juan Fernandez

I am monarch of all I survey,
    My right there is none to dispute,
From the centre all round to the sea,
    I am lord of the fowl and the brute.
Oh solitude! where are the charms
    That sages have seen in thy face?
Better dwell in the midst of alarms,
    Than reign in this horrible place.

I am out of humanity's reach,
    I must finish my journey alone,
Never hear the sweet music of speech,
    I start at the sound of my own.
The beasts that roam over the plain,
    My form with indifference see,
They are so unacquainted with man,
    Their tameness is shocking to me.

Society, friendship, and love,
    Divinely bestowed upon man,
Oh had I the wings of a dove,
    How soon would I taste you again!
My sorrows I then might assuage,
    In the ways of religion and truth,
Might learn from the wisdom of age,
    And be cheered by the sallies of youth.

Religion! what treasure untold
    Resides in that heavenly word!
More precious than silver and gold,
    Or all that this earth can afford.
But the sound of the church-going bell
    These vallies and rocks never heard,
Ne'er sighed at the sound of a knell,
    Or smiled when a sabbath appeared.

Ye winds that have made me your sport,
    Convey to this desolate shore,
Some cordial endearing report
    Of a land I shall visit no more.
My friends do they now and then send
    A wish or a thought after me?
O tell me I yet have a friend,
    Though a friend I am never to see.

How fleet is a glance of the mind!
    Compared with the speed of its flight,
The tempest itself lags behind,
    And the swift wingèd arrows of light.

When I think of my own native land,
 In a moment I seem to be there;
But alas! recollection at hand
 Soon hurries me back to despair.

But the sea fowl is gone to her nest,
 The beast is laid down in his lair,
Even here is a season of rest,
 And I to my cabin repair.
There is mercy in every place,
 And mercy, encouraging thought!
Gives even affliction a grace,
 And reconciles man to his lot.

WILLIAM COWPER

The Footprint in the Sand

It happened one day about noon going towards my boat, I was exceedingly surprized with the print of a man's naked foot on the shore, which was very plain to be seen in the sand. I stood like one thunder-struck, or as if I had seen an apparition; I listened, I looked round me, I could hear nothing, nor see any thing; I went up to a rising ground to look farther; I went up the shore and down the shore, but it was all one, I could see no other impression but that one. I went to it again to see if there were any more, and to observe if it might not be my fancy; but there was no room for that, for there was exactly the very print of a foot, toes, heel, and every part of a foot; how it came thither I knew not, nor could in the least imagine. But after innumerable fluttering thoughts, like a man perfectly confused and out of my self, I came home to my fortification, not feeling, as we say, the ground I went on, but terrify'd to the last degree, looking behind me at every two or three steps, mistaking every bush and tree, and fancying every stump at a distance to be a man; nor is it possible to describe how many various shapes affrighted imagination represented things to me in, how many wild ideas were found every moment in my fancy, and what strange unaccountable whimsies came into my thoughts by the way.

When I came to my castle, for so I think I called it ever after this, I fled into it like one pursued; whether I went over by the ladder as first contrived, or went in at the hole in the rock which I called a door, I cannot remember; no, nor could I remember the next morning, for never frighted hare fled to cover, or fox to earth, with more terror of mind than I to this retreat.

I slept none that night; the farther I was from the occasion of my fright, the greater my apprehensions were, which is something contrary to the nature of such things, and especially to the usual practice of all creatures in fear: but I was so embarrassed with my own frightful ideas of the thing, that I formed nothing but dismal imaginations to my self, even tho' I was not a great way off of it. Sometimes I fancy'd it must be the devil; and reason joyned in with me upon this supposition; for how should any other thing in human shape come into the place? Where was the vessel that brought them? What marks was there of any other footsteps? And how was it possible a man should come there? But then to think that Satan should take human shape upon him in such a place where there could be no manner of occasion for it, but to leave the print of his foot behind him, and that even for no purpose too, for he could not be sure I should see it; this was an amusement the other way; I considered that the devil might have found out abundance of other ways to have terrify'd me than this of the single print of a foot; that as I lived quite on the other side of the island, he would never have been so simple to leave a mark in a place where 'twas ten thousand to one whether I should ever see it or not, and in the sand too, which the first surge of the sea upon a high wind would have defaced entirely. All this seemed inconsistent with the thing it self, and with all the notions we usually entertain of the subtilty of the devil.

Abundance of such things as these assisted to argue me out of all apprehensions of its being the devil; and I presently concluded then, that it must be some more dangerous creature, viz. that it must be some of the savages of the main land over-against me, who had wandered out to sea in their canoes, and, either driven by the currents or by contrary winds, had made the island; and had been on shore, but were gone away again to sea, being as loth, perhaps, to have stayed in this desolate island as I would have been to have had them.

While these reflections were rowling upon my mind, I was very thankful in my thoughts that I was so happy as not to be thereabouts at that time, or that they did not see my boat, by which they would have concluded that some inhabitants had been in the place, and perhaps have searched farther for me. Then terrible thoughts racked my imagination about their having found my boat, and that there were people here; and that if so, I should certainly have them come again in greater numbers, and devour me; that if it should happen so that they should not find me, yet they would find my enclosure, destroy all my corn, carry away all my flock of tame goats, and I should perish at last for meer want.

Thus my fear banished all my religious hope; all that former confidence in God, which was founded upon such wonderful experience as I had had of His goodness, now vanished, as if He that had fed me by miracle hitherto, could not preserve by His power the provision which He had made for me by His goodness. I reproached myself with my easiness, that would not sow any more corn one year than would just serve me till the next season, as if no accident could intervene to prevent my enjoying the crop that was upon the ground; and this I thought so just a reproof, that I resolved for the future to have two or three years corn beforehand, so that whatever might come, I might not perish for want of bread.

How strange a chequer work of providence is the life of man! and by what secret differing springs are the affections hurry'd about as differing circumstances present! To day we love what to morrow we hate; to day we seek what to morrow we shun; to day we desire what to morrow we fear, nay, even tremble at the apprehensions of; this was exemplify'd in me at this time in the most lively manner imaginable; for I whose only affliction was, that I seemed banished from human society, that I was alone, circumscribed by the boundless ocean, cut off from mankind, and condemned to what I called silent life; that I was as one who Heaven thought not worthy to be numbered among the living, or to appear among the rest of His creatures; that to have seen one of my own species would have seemed to me a raising from death to life, and the greatest blessing that Heaven it self, next to the supreme blessing of salvation, could bestow; I say, that I should now tremble at the very apprehensions of seeing a man, and was ready to sink into the ground at but the shadow or silent appearance of a man's having set his foot in the island.

DANIEL DEFOE
from *Robinson Crusoe*

Bermudas

> Where the remote Bermudas ride
> In the ocean's bosom unespied,
> From a small boat, that rowed along,
> The listening winds received this song.

'What should we do but sing his praise
That led us through the watery maze,
Unto an isle so long unknown,
And yet far kinder than our own?
Where he the huge sea-monsters wracks,
That lift the deep upon their backs,
He lands us on a grassy stage,
Safe from the storms, and prelate's rage.
He gave us this eternal spring,
Which here enamels everything,
And sends the fowl to us in care,
On daily visits through the air.
He hangs in shades the orange bright,
Like golden lamps in a green night,
And does in the pom'granates close
Jewels more rich than Ormus shows.
He makes the figs our mouths to meet,
And throws the melons at our feet,
But apples plants of such a price,
No tree could ever bear them twice.
With cedars, chosen by his hand,
From Lebanon, he stores the land,
And makes the hollow seas, that roar,
Proclaim the ambergris on shore.
He cast (of which we rather boast)
The gospel's pearl upon our coast,
And in these rocks for us did frame
A temple, where to sound his name.
Oh let our voice his praise exalt,
Till it arrive at heaven's vault:
Which thence (perhaps) rebounding, may
Echo beyond the Mexique Bay.'

Thus sung they, in the English boat,
An holy and a cheerful note,
And all the way, to guide their chime,
With falling oars they kept the time.

ANDREW MARVELL

To the Man-of-War Bird

Thou who hast slept all night upon the storm,
Waking renew'd on thy prodigious pinions,
(Burst the wild storm? above it thou ascended'st,
And rested on the sky, thy slave that cradled thee,)
Now a blue point, far, far, in heaven floating,
As to the light emerging here on deck I watch thee,
(Myself a speck, a point on the world's floating vast.)

Far, far at sea,
After the night's fierce drifts have strewn the shore with
    wrecks,
With re-appearing day as now so happy and serene,
The rosy and elastic dawn, the flashing sun,
The limpid spread of air cerulean,
Thou also re-appearest.

Thou born to match the gale, (thou art all wings,)
To cope with heaven and earth and sea and hurricane,
Thou ship of air that never furl'st thy sails,
Days, even weeks untired and onward, through spaces, realms
    gyrating,
At dusk that look'st on Senegal, at morn America,

That sport'st amid the lightning-flash and thunder-cloud,
In them, in thy experiences, had'st thou my soul,
What joys! what joys were thine!

WALT WHITMAN

The Jumblies

They went to sea in a Sieve, they did,
   In a Sieve they went to sea:
In spite of all their friends could say,
   On a winter's morn, on a stormy day,
     In a Sieve they went to sea!
And when the Sieve turned round and round,
And every one cried, 'You'll all be drowned!'
They called aloud, 'Our Sieve ain't big,
But we don't care a button! we don't care a fig!
   In a Sieve we'll go to sea!'
     Far and few, far and few,
      Are the lands where the Jumblies live;
      Their heads are green, and their hands are blue,
      And they went to sea in a Sieve.

They sailed away in a Sieve, they did,
   In a Sieve they sailed so fast,
With only a beautiful pea-green veil
Tied with a riband by way of a sail,
   To a small tobacco-pipe mast;
And every one said, who saw them go,
'O won't they be soon upset, you know!
For the sky is dark, and the voyage is long,
And happen what may, it's extremely wrong
   In a Sieve to sail so fast!'

Far and few, far and few,
　　Are the lands where the Jumblies live,
　　Their heads are green, and their hands are blue,
　　　And they went to sea in a Sieve.

The water it soon came in, it did,
　The water it soon came in;
So to keep them dry, they wrapped their feet
In a pinky paper all folded neat,
　And they fastened it down with a pin.
And they passed the night in a crockery-jar,
And each of them said, 'How wise we are!
Though the sky be dark, and the voyage be long,
Yet we never can think we were rash or wrong,
　While round in our Sieve we spin!'
　　Far and few, far and few,
　　　Are the lands where the Jumblies live;
　　Their heads are green, and their hands are blue,
　　　And they went to sea in a Sieve.

And all night long they sailed away;
　And when the sun went down,
They whistled and warbled a moony song
To the echoing sound of a coppery gong,
　In the shade of the mountains brown.
'O Timballo! How happy we are,
When we live in a sieve and a crockery-jar,
And all night long in the moonlight pale,
We sail away with a pea-green sail,
　In the shade of the mountains brown!'
　　Far and few, far and few,
　　　Are the lands where the Jumblies live;
　　Their heads are green, and their hands are blue,
　　　And they went to sea in a Sieve.

They sailed to the Western Sea, they did,
　To a land all covered with trees,
And they bought an Owl, and a useful Cart,
And a pound of Rice, and a Cranberry Tart,
　And a hive of silvery Bees.
And they bought a Pig, and some green Jack-daws,
And a lovely Monkey with lollipop paws,
And forty bottles of Ring-Bo-Ree,
　And no end of Stilton Cheese.
　Far and few, far and few,
　　Are the lands where the Jumblies live;
　Their heads are green, and their hands are blue,
　　And they went to sea in a Sieve.

EDWARD LEAR

Squid

Slowly wading through the meadows of brit, the Pequod still held on her way north-eastward towards the island of Java; a gentle air impelling her keel, so that in the surrounding serenity her three tall tapering masts mildly waved to that languid breeze, as three mild palms on a plain. And still, at wide intervals in the silvery night, the lonely, alluring jet would be seen.

But one transparent blue morning, when a stillness almost preternatural spread over the sea, however unattended with any stagnant calm; when the long burnished sun-glade on the waters seemed a golden finger laid across them, enjoining some secresy; when the slippered waves whispered together as they softly ran on; in this profound hush of the visible sphere a strange spectre was seen by Daggoo from the main-mast-head.

In the distance, a great white mass lazily rose, and rising higher and higher, and disentangling itself from the azure, at last gleamed before our prow like a snow-slide, new slid from the hills. Thus glistening for a moment, as slowly it subsided, and sank. Then once more arose, and silently gleamed. It seemed not a whale; and yet is this Moby Dick? thought Daggoo. Again the phantom went down, but on re-appearing once more, with a stiletto-like cry that startled every man from his nod, the negro yelled out – 'There! there again! there she breaches! right ahead! The White Whale, the White Whale!'

Upon this, the seamen rushed to the yard-arms, as in swarming-time the bees rush to the boughs. Bare-headed in the sultry sun, Ahab stood on the bowsprit, and with one hand pushed far behind in readiness to wave his orders to the helmsman, cast his eager glance in the direction indicated aloft by the outstretched motionless arm of Daggoo.

Whether the flitting attendance of the one still and solitary jet had gradually worked upon Ahab, so that he was now prepared to connect the ideas of mildness and repose with the first sight of the particular whale he pursued; however this was, or whether his eagerness betrayed him; whichever way it might have been, no sooner did he distinctly perceive the white mass, than with a quick intensity he instantly gave orders for lowering.

The four boats were soon on the water; Ahab's in advance, and all swiftly pulling towards their prey. Soon it went down, and while, with oars suspended, we were awaiting its reappearance, lo! in the same spot where it sank, once more it slowly rose. Almost forgetting for the moment all thoughts of Moby Dick, we now gazed at the most wondrous phenomenon which the secret seas have hitherto revealed to mankind. A vast pulpy mass, furlongs in length and breadth, of a glancing cream-color, lay floating on the water, innumerable long arms radiating from its centre, and curling and twisting like a nest of anacondas, as if blindly to clutch at any hapless object within reach. No perceptible face or front did it have; no conceivable token of either sensation or instinct; but undulated there on the billows, an unearthly formless, chance-like apparition of life.

As with a low sucking sound it slowly disappeared again, Starbuck still gazing at the agitated waters where it had sunk, with a wild voice exclaimed – 'Almost rather had I seen Moby Dick and fought him, than to have seen thee, thou white ghost!'

'What was it, Sir?' said Flask.

'The great live squid, which, they say, few whale-ships ever beheld, and returned to their ports to tell of it.'

But Ahab said nothing; turning his boat, he sailed back to the vessel; the rest as silently following.

Whatever superstitions the sperm whalemen in general have connected with the sight of this object, certain it is, that a glimpse of it being so very unusual, that circumstance has gone far to invest it with portentousness. So rarely is it beheld, that though one and all of them declare it to be the largest animated thing in the ocean, yet very few of them have any but the most vague ideas concerning its true nature and form; notwithstanding, they believe it to furnish to the sperm whale his only food. For though other species of whales find their food above water, and may be seen by man in the act of feeding, the spermaceti whale obtains his whole food in unknown zones below the surface; and only by inference is it that any one can tell of what, precisely, that food consists. At times, when closely pursued, he will disgorge what are supposed to be the detached arms of the squid; some of them thus exhibited exceeding twenty and thirty feet in length. They fancy that the monster to which these arms belonged ordinarily clings by them to the bed of the ocean; and that the sperm whale, unlike other species, is supplied with teeth in order to attack and tear it.

There seems some ground to imagine that the great Kraken of Bishop Pontoppidan may ultimately resolve itself into Squid. The manner in which the Bishop describes it, as alternately rising and sinking, with some other particulars he narrates, in all this the two correspond. But much abatement is necessary with respect to the incredible bulk he assigns it.

By some naturalists who have vaguely heard rumors of the mysterious creature, here spoken of, it is included among the class of cuttle-fish, to which, indeed, in certain external respects it would seem to belong, but only as the Anak of the tribe.

HERMAN MELVILLE
from *Moby-Dick*

By Steamer to Cagliari

The ship was almost empty – save of course for the street-corner louts who hung about just below, on the deck itself. We stood alone on the weather-faded little promenade deck, which has old oak seats with old, carved little lions at the ends, for arm-rests – and a little cabin mysteriously shut, which much peeping determined as the wireless office and the operator's little curtained bed-niche.

Cold, fresh wind, a black-blue, translucent, rolling sea on which the wake rose in snapping foam, and Sicily on the left: Monte Pellegrino, a huge, inordinate mass of pinkish rock, hardly crisped with the faintest vegetation, looming up to heaven from the sea. Strangely large in mass and bulk Monte Pellegrino looks: and bare, like a Sahara in heaven: and old-looking. These coasts of Sicily are very imposing, terrific, fortifying the interior. And again one gets the feeling that age has worn them bare: as if old, old civilisations had worn away and exhausted the soil, leaving a terrifying blankness of rock, as at Syracuse in plateaus, and here in great mass.

There seems hardly anyone on board but ourselves: we alone on the little promenade deck. Strangely lonely, floating on a bare old ship past the great bare shores, on a rolling sea, stooping and rising in the wind. The wood on the fittings is all bare and weather-silvered, the cabin, the seats, even the little lions of the seats. The paint wore away long ago: and this timber will never see paint any more. Strange to put one's hand on the old oaken wood, so sea-fibred. Good old delicate-threaded oak: I swear it grew in England. And everything so carefully done, so solidly and everlastingly. I look at the lions, with the perfect-fitting oaken pins through their paws clinching them down, and their little mouths open. They are as solid as they were in Victorian days, as immovable. They will never wear away. What a joy in the careful, thorough, manly, everlasting work put into a ship: at least into this sixty-year-old vessel. Every bit of this old oak wood so sound, so beautiful: and the whole welded together with joints and wooden pins far more beautifully and livingly than iron welds. Rustless, life-born, living-tissued old wood: rustless as flesh is rustless, and happy-seeming as iron never can be. She rides so well, she takes the sea so beautifully, as a matter of course.

D. H. LAWRENCE
from *Sea and Sardinia*

After the Sea-Ship

After the sea-ship, after the whistling winds,
After the white-gray sails taut to their spars and ropes,
Below, a myriad myriad waves hastening, lifting up their
    necks,
Tending in ceaseless flow toward the track of the ship,
Waves of the ocean bubbling and gurgling, blithely prying,
Waves, undulating waves, liquid, uneven, emulous waves,
Toward that whirling current, laughing and buoyant, with
    curves,
Where the great vessel sailing and tacking displaces the
    surface,

Larger and smaller waves in the spread of the ocean
    yearnfully flowing,
The wake of the sea-ship after she passes, flashing and
    frolicsome under the sun,
A motley procession with many a fleck of foam and many
    fragments,
Following the stately and rapid ship, in the wake following.

WALT WHITMAN

Equipping a Whaler

The request of an honest merchant to a friend of his,
to be advised and directed in the course of killing the
whale. An. 1575. These requests were thus answered.

A proportion for the setting forth of a ship of 200 tons, for the
killing of the whale.
There must be 55 men who departing for Wardhouse in the
month of April, must be furnished with 4 quintals and a half
of bread for every man.
250 hogsheads to put the bread in.
150 hogsheads of cider.
6 quintals of oil.
8 quintals of bacon.
6 hogsheads of beef.
10 quarters of salt.
150 pound of candles.
8 quarters of beans and peas.
Saltfish and herring, a quantity convenient.
4 tuns of wines.
Half a quarter of mustard seed, and a quern.
A grindstone.

800 empty shaken hogsheads.

350 bundles of hoops.

800 pairs of heads for the hogsheads.

10 estachas for harpoon irons.

3 pieces of baibens for the javelins small.

2 tackles to turn the whales.

A hawser of 27 fathoms long to turn the whales.

15 great javelins.

18 small javelins.

50 harpoon irons.

6 machicos to cut the whale withall.

2 dozen of machetos to mince the whale.

2 great hooks to turn the whale.

3 pair of canhooks.

6 hooks for staves.

3 dozen of staves for the harpoon irons.

6 pulleys to turn the whale with.

10 great baskets.

10 lamps of iron to carry light.

5 kettles of 150 lbs the piece, and 6 ladles.

1000 of nails for the pinnaces.

500 of nails for the houses, and the wharf.

18 axes and hatchets to cleave wood.

12 pieces of lines, and 6 dozen of hooks.

2 beetles of rosemary.

4 dozen of oars for the pinnaces.

6 lanterns.

Item, gunpowder and matches for arquebuses as shall be needful.

Item, there must be carried from hence 5 pinnaces, five men to strike with harpoon irons, two cutters of whale, 5 coopers, and a purser or two.

RICHARD HAKLUYT
from *Voyages and Discoveries*

Log of the Demeter

Varna to Whitby
Written 18 July, things so strange happening, that I
shall keep accurate note henceforth till we land

On 6 July we finished taking in cargo, silver sand and boxes of earth. At noon set sail. East wind, fresh. Crew, five hands, . . . two mates, cook, and myself (captain).

On 11 July at dawn entered Bosphorus. Boarded by Turkish Customs officers. Backsheesh. All correct. Under way at 4 p.m.

On 12 July through Dardanelles. More Customs officers and flagboat of guarding squadron. Backsheesh again. Work of officers thorough, but quick. Want us off soon. At dark passed into Archipelago.

On 13 July passed Cape Matapan. Crew dissatisfied about something. Seemed scared, but would not speak out.

On 14 July was somewhat anxious about crew. Men all steady fellows, who sailed with me before. Mate could not make out what was wrong; they only told him there was *something*, and crossed themselves. Mate lost temper with one of them that day and struck him. Expected fierce quarrel, but all was quiet.

On 16 July mate reported in the morning that one of crew, Petrofsky, was missing. Could not account for it. Took larboard watch eight bells last night; was relieved by Abramoff, but did not go to bunk. Men more downcast than ever. All said they expected something of the kind, but would not say more than that there was *something* aboard. Mate getting very impatient with them; feared some trouble ahead.

On 17 July, yesterday, one of the men, Olgaren, came to my cabin, and in an awestruck way confided to me that he thought there was a strange man aboard the ship. He said that in his watch he had been sheltering behind the deck-house, and there was a rain-storm, when he saw a tall, thin man, who was not like any of the crew, come up the companion-way, and go along the deck forward, and disappear. He followed cautiously, but when he got to bows found no one, and the hatchways were all closed. He was in a panic of superstitious fear, and I am afraid the panic may spread. To allay it, I shall today search entire ship carefully from stem to stern.

Later in the day I got together the whole crew, and told them, as they evidently thought there was some one in the ship, we would search from stem to stern. First mate angry; said it was folly, and to yield to such foolish ideas would demoralize the men; said he would engage to keep them out of trouble with a handspike. I let him take the helm, while the rest began thorough search, all keeping abreast, with lanterns; we left no corner unsearched. As there were only the big wooden boxes, there were no odd corners where a man could hide. Men much relieved when search over, and went back to work cheerfully. First mate scowled, but said nothing.

22 July. – Rough weather last three days, and all hands busy with sails – no time to be frightened. Men seem to have forgotten their dread. Mate cheerful again, and all on good terms. Praised men for work in bad weather. Passed Gibraltar and out through Straits. All well.

24 July. – There seems some doom over this ship. Already a hand short, and entering on the Bay of Biscay with wild weather ahead, and yet last night another man lost – disappeared. Like the first, he came off his watch and was not seen again. Men all in a panic of fear; sent a round robin, asking to have double watch, as they fear to be alone. Mate violent. Fear there will be some trouble, as either he or the men will do some violence.

28 July. – Four days in hell, knocking about in a sort of maelstrom, and the wind a tempest. No sleep for any one. Men all worn out. Hardly know how to set a watch, since no one fit to go on. Second mate volunteered to steer and watch, and let men snatch a few hours' sleep. Wind abating; seas still terrific, but feel them less, as ship is steadier.

29 July. – Another tragedy. Had single watch tonight, as crew too tired to double. When morning watch came on deck could find no one except steersman. Raised outcry, and all came on deck. Thorough search, but no one found. Are now without second mate, and crew in a panic. Mate and I agreed to go armed henceforth and wait for any sign of cause.

30 July. – Last night. Rejoiced we are nearing England. Weather fine, all sails set. Retired worn out; slept soundly; awaked by mate telling me that both man of watch and steersman missing. Only self and mate and two hands left to work ship.

1 August. – Two days of fog, and not a sail sighted. Had hoped when in the English Channel to be able to signal for help or get in somewhere. Not having power to work sails, have to run before wind. Dare not lower, as could not raise them again. We seem to be drifting to some terrible doom. Mate now more demoralized than either of men. His stronger nature seems to have worked inwardly against himself. Men are beyond fear, working stolidly and patiently, with minds made up to worst. They are Russian, he Roumanian.

2 August, midnight. – Woke up from few minutes' sleep by hearing a cry, seemingly outside my port. Could see nothing in fog. Rushed on deck, and ran against mate. Tells me heard cry and ran, but no sign of man on watch. One more gone. Lord, help us! Mate says we must be past Straits of Dover, as in a moment of fog lifting he saw North Foreland, just as he heard the man cry out. If so we are now off in the North Sea, and only God can guide us in the fog, which seems to move with us; and God seems to have deserted us.

3 August. – At midnight I went to relieve the man at the wheel, but when I got to it found no one there. The wind was steady, and as we ran before it there was no yawing. I dared not leave it, so shouted for the mate. After a few seconds he rushed up on deck in his flannels. He looked wild-eyed and haggard, and I greatly fear his reason has given way. He came close to me and whispered hoarsely, with his mouth to my ear, as though fearing the very air might hear: '*It* is here; I know it, now. On the watch last night I saw It, like a man, tall and thin, and ghastly pale. It was in the bows, and looking out. I crept behind It, and gave It my knife; but the knife went through It, empty as the air.' And as he spoke he took his knife and drove it savagely into space. Then he went on: 'But It is here, and I'll find It. It is in the hold, perhaps, in one of those boxes. I'll unscrew them one by one and see. You work the helm.' And with a warning look and his finger on his lip, he went below. There was springing up a choppy wind, and I could not leave the helm. I saw him come out on deck again with a tool-chest and a lantern, and go down the forward hatchway. He is mad, stark, raving mad, and it's no use my trying to stop him. He can't hurt those big boxes: they are invoiced as 'clay,' and to pull them about is as harmless a thing as he can do. So here I stay, and mind the helm, and write these notes. I can only trust in God and wait till the fog clears. Then, if I can't steer to any harbour with the wind that is, I shall cut down sails and lie by, and signal for help . . .

It is nearly all over now. Just as I was beginning to hope that the mate would come out calmer – for I heard him knocking away at something in the hold, and work is good for him – there came up the hatchway a sudden, startled scream, which made my blood run cold, and up on the deck he came as if shot from a gun – a raging madman, with his eyes rolling and his face convulsed with fear. 'Save me! save me!' he cried, and then looked round on the blanket of fog. His horror turned to despair, and in a steady voice he said: 'You had better come too, captain, before it is too late. *He* is there. I know the secret now. The sea will save me from Him, and it is all that is left!' Before I could say a word, or move forward to seize him, he sprang on the bulwark and deliberately threw himself into the sea. I suppose I know the secret too, now. It was this madman who had got rid of the men one by one, and now he has followed them himself. God help me! How am I to account for all these horrors when I get to port? *When* I get to port! Will that ever be?

4 August. – Still fog, which the sunrise cannot pierce. I know there is sunrise because I am a sailor, why else I know not. I dared not go below, I dared not leave the helm; so here all night I stayed, and in the dimness of the night I saw It – Him! God forgive me, but the mate was right to jump overboard. It is better to die like a man; to die like a sailor in blue water no man can object. But I am captain, and I must not leave my ship. But I shall baffle this fiend or monster, for I shall tie my hands to the wheel when my strength begins to fail, and along with them I shall tie that which He – It! – dare not touch; and then, come good wind or foul, I shall save my soul, and my honour as a captain. I am growing weaker, and the night is coming on. If He can look me in the face again, I may not have time to act ... If we are wrecked, mayhap this bottle may be found, and those who find it may understand; if not, . . . well, then all men shall know that I have been true to my trust. God and the Blessed Virgin and the saints help a poor ignorant soul trying to do his duty . . .

BRAM STOKER
from *Dracula*

Shipwreck

I descended to the lower deck. The *Martinez* was sinking fast, for the water was very near. Numbers of the passengers were leaping overboard. Others, in the water, were clamoring to be taken aboard again. No one heeded them. A cry arose that we were sinking. I was seized by the consequent panic, and went over the side in a surge of bodies. How I went over I do not know, though I did know, and instantly, why those in the water were so desirous of getting back on the steamer. The water was cold – so cold that it was painful. The pang, as I plunged into it, was as quick and sharp as that of fire. It bit to the marrow. It was like the grip of death. I gasped with the anguish and shock of it, filling my lungs before the life-preserver popped me to the surface. The taste of the salt was strong in my mouth, and I was strangling with the acrid stuff in my throat and lungs.

But it was the cold that was most distressing. I felt that I could survive but a few minutes. People were struggling and floundering in the water about me. I could hear them crying out to one another. And I heard, also, the sound of oars. Evidently the strange steamboat had lowered its boats. As the time went by I marvelled that I was still alive. I had no sensation whatever in my lower limbs, while a chilling numbness was wrapping about my heart and creeping into it. Small waves, with spiteful foaming crests, continually broke over me and into my mouth, sending me off into more strangling paroxysms.

The noises grew indistinct, though I heard a final and despairing chorus of screams in the distance, and knew that the *Martinez* had gone down. Later – how much later I have no knowledge – I came to myself with a start of fear. I was alone. I could hear no calls or cries – only the sound of the waves, made weirdly hollow and reverberant by the fog. A panic in a crowd, which partakes of a sort of community of interest, is not so terrible as a panic when one is by oneself; and such a panic I now suffered. Whither was I drifting? The red-faced man had said that the tide was ebbing through the Golden Gate. Was I, then, being carried out to sea? And the life-preserver in which I floated? Was it not liable to go to pieces at any moment? I had heard of such things being made of paper and hollow rushes which quickly became saturated and lost all buoyancy. And I could not swim a stroke. And I was alone, floating, apparently, in the midst of a gray primordial vastness. I confess that a madness seized me, that I shrieked aloud as the women had shrieked, and beat the water with my numb hands.

JACK LONDON
from *The Sea-Wolf*

An Atlantic Gale

Once – once – I found myself on deck. I don't know how I got there, or what possessed me to go there, but there I was; and completely dressed too, with a huge pea-coat on, and a pair of boots such as no weak man in his senses could ever have got into. I found myself standing, when a gleam of consciousness came upon me, holding on to something. I don't know what. I think it was the boatswain: or it may have been the pump: or possibly the cow. I can't say how long I had been there; whether a day or a minute. I recollect trying to think about something (about anything in the whole wide world, I was not particular) without the smallest effect. I could not even make out which was the sea, and which the sky, for the horizon seemed drunk, and was flying wildly about, in all directions. Even in that incapable state, however, I recognised the lazy gentleman standing before me: nautically clad in a suit of shaggy blue, with an oilskin hat. But I was too imbecile, although I knew it to be he, to separate him from his dress; and tried to call him, I remember, *Pilot*. After another interval of total unconsciousness, I found he had gone, and recognised another figure in its place. It seemed to wave and fluctuate before me as though I saw it reflected in an unsteady looking-glass; but I knew it for the captain; and such was the cheerful influence of his face, that I tried to smile:

yes, even then I tried to smile. I saw by his gestures that he addressed me; but it was a long time before I could make out that he remonstrated against my standing up to my knees in water – as I was; of course I don't know why. I tried to thank him, but couldn't. I could only point to my boots – or wherever I supposed my boots to be – and say in a plaintive voice, 'Cork soles:' at the same time endeavouring, I am told, to sit down in the pool. Finding that I was quite insensible, and for the time a maniac, he humanely conducted me below.

There I remained until I got better: suffering, whenever I was recommended to eat anything, an amount of anguish only second to that which is said to be endured by the apparently drowned, in the process of restoration to life. One gentleman on board had a letter of introduction to me from a mutual friend in London. He sent it below with his card, on the morning of the head-wind; and I was long troubled with the idea that he might be up, and well, and a hundred times a day expecting me to call upon him in the saloon. I imagined him one of those cast-iron images – I will not call them men – who ask, with red faces, and lusty voices, what sea-sickness means, and whether it really is as bad as it is represented to be. This was very torturing indeed; and I don't think I ever felt such perfect gratification and gratitude of heart, as I did when I heard from the ship's doctor that he had been obliged to put a large mustard poultice on this very gentleman's stomach. I date my recovery from the receipt of that intelligence.

It was materially assisted though, I have no doubt, by a heavy gale of wind, which came slowly up at sunset, when we were about ten days out, and raged with gradually increasing fury until morning, saving that it lulled for an hour a little before midnight. There was something in the unnatural repose of that hour, and in the after gathering of the storm, so inconceivably awful and tremendous, that its bursting into full violence was almost a relief.

The labouring of the ship in the troubled sea on this night I shall never forget. 'Will it ever be worse than this?' was a question I had often heard asked, when everything was sliding and bumping about, and when it certainly did seem difficult to comprehend the possibility of anything afloat being more disturbed, without toppling over and going down. But what the agitation of a steam-vessel is, on a bad winter's night in the wild Atlantic, it is impossible for the most vivid imagination to conceive. To say that she is flung down on her side in the waves, with her masts dipping into them, and that, springing up again, she rolls over on the other side, until a heavy sea strikes her with the noise of a hundred great guns, and hurls her back – that she stops, and staggers, and shivers, as though stunned, and then, with a violent throbbing at her heart, darts onward like a monster goaded into madness, to be beaten down, and battered, and crushed, and leaped on by the angry sea – that thunder, lightning, hail, and rain, and wind, are all in fierce contention for the mastery – that every plank has its groan, every nail its shriek, and every drop of water in the great ocean its howling voice – is nothing. To say that all is grand, and all appalling and horrible in the last degree, is nothing. Words cannot express it. Thoughts cannot convey it. Only a dream can call it up again, in all its fury, rage, and passion.

And yet, in the very midst of these terrors, I was placed in a situation so exquisitely ridiculous, that even then I had as strong a sense of its absurdity as I have now, and could no more help laughing than I can at any other comical incident, happening under circumstances the most favourable to its enjoyment. About midnight we shipped a sea, which forced its way through the skylights, burst open the doors above, and came raging and roaring down into the ladies' cabin, to the unspeakable consternation of my wife and a little Scotch lady – who, by the way, had previously sent a message to the captain by the stewardess, requesting him, with her compliments, to have a steel conductor immediately attached to the top of every mast, and to the chimney, in order that the ship might not be struck by lightning. They, and the handmaid before mentioned, being in such ecstasies of fear that I scarcely knew what to do with them, I naturally bethought myself of some restorative or comfortable cordial; and nothing better occurring to me, at the moment, than hot brandy-and-water, I procured a tumbler-full without delay. It being impossible to stand or sit without holding on, they were all heaped together in one corner of a long sofa – a fixture extending entirely across the cabin – where they clung to each other in momentary expectation of being drowned. When I approached this place with my specific, and was about to administer it, with many consolatory expressions, to the nearest sufferer, what was my dismay to see them all roll slowly down to the other end! And when I staggered to that end, and held out the glass once more, how immensely baffled were my good intentions by the ship giving another lurch, and their all rolling back again! I suppose I dodged them up and down this sofa, for at least a quarter of an hour, without reaching them once; and by the time I did catch them, the brandy-and-water was diminished, by constant spilling, to a teaspoonful. To complete the group, it is necessary to recognise in this disconcerted dodger, a very pale individual, who had shaved his beard and brushed his hair, last, at Liverpool: and whose only articles of dress (linen not included) were a pair of dreadnought trousers; a blue jacket, formerly admired upon the Thames at Richmond; no stockings; and one slipper.

Of the outrageous antics performed by that ship next morning; which made bed a practical joke, and getting up, by any process short of falling out, an impossibility; I say nothing. But anything like the utter dreariness and desolation that met my eyes when I, literally, 'tumbled up' on deck at noon, I never saw. Ocean and sky were all of one dull, heavy, uniform, lead colour. There was no extent of prospect even over the dreary waste that lay around us, for the sea ran high, and the horizon encompassed us like a large black hoop. Viewed from the air, or some tall bluff on shore, it would have been imposing and stupendous no doubt; but seen from the wet and rolling decks, it only impressed one giddily and painfully. In the gale of last night the life-boat had been crushed by one blow of the sea like a walnut-shell; and there it hung dangling in the air: a mere faggot of crazy boards. The planking of the paddle-boxes had been torn sheer away. The wheels were exposed and bare; and they whirled and dashed their spray about the decks at random. Chimney, white with crusted salt; topmasts struck; stormsails set; rigging all knotted, tangled, wet, and drooping: a gloomier picture it would be hard to look upon.

CHARLES DICKENS
from *American Notes*

The Privations of Sea Travel

Our voyage having come to an end, I will take a short retrospect of the advantages and disadvantages, the pains and pleasures, of our five years' wandering. If a person should ask my advice, before undertaking a long voyage, my answer would depend upon his possessing a decided taste for some branch of knowledge, which could by such means be improved. No doubt it is a high satisfaction to behold various countries, and the many races of mankind, but the pleasures gained at the time do not counterbalance the evils. It is necessary to look forward to a harvest, however distant it may be, when some fruit will be reaped, some good effected.

Many of the losses which must be experienced are obvious; such as that of the society of all old friends, and of the sight of those places, with which every dearest remembrance is so intimately connected. These losses, however, are at the time partly relieved by the exhaustless delight of anticipating the long wished-for day of return. If, as poets say, life is a dream, I am sure in a voyage these are the visions which serve best to pass away the long night. Other losses, although not at first felt, tell heavily after a period; these are, the want of room, of seclusion, of rest; the jading feeling of constant hurry; the privation of small luxuries, the comforts of civilization and domestic society, and, lastly, even of music and the other pleasures of imagination. When such trifles are mentioned, it is evident that the real grievances (excepting from accidents) of a sea life are at an end. The short space of sixty years has made an astonishing difference in the facility of distant navigation. Even in the time of Cook, a man who left his comfortable fireside for such expeditions, underwent severe privations. A yacht now with every luxury of life might circumnavigate the globe. Besides the vast improvements in ships and naval resources, the whole western shores of America are thrown open, and Australia has become the metropolis of a rising continent. How different are the circumstances to a man shipwrecked at the present day in the Pacific, to what they were in the time of Cook! Since his voyage a hemisphere has been added to the civilized world.

If a person suffer much from sea-sickness, let him weigh it heavily in the balance. I speak from experience: it is no trifling evil which may be cured in a week. If, on the other hand, he takes pleasure in naval tactics, he will assuredly have full scope for his taste. But it must be borne in mind, how large a proportion of the time, during a long voyage, is spent on the water, as compared with the days in harbour. And what are the boasted glories of the illimitable ocean? A tedious waste, a desert of water, as the Arabian calls it. No doubt there are some delightful scenes. A moonlight night, with the clear heavens and the dark glittering sea, and the white sails filled by the soft air of a gently-blowing trade wind; a dead calm, with the heaving surface polished like a mirror, and all still, except the occasional flapping of the sails. It is well once to behold a squall with its rising arch and coming fury, or the heavy gale of wind and mountainous waves. I confess, however, my imagination had painted something more grand, more terrific in the full-grown storm. It is an incomparably finer spectacle when beheld on shore, where the waving trees, the wild flight of the birds, the dark shadows and bright lights, the rushing of the torrents, all proclaim the strife of the unloosed elements. At sea the albatross and petrel fly as if the storm were their proper sphere, the water rises and sinks as if fulfilling its usual task, the ship alone and its inhabitants seem the objects of wrath. On a forlorn and weather-beaten coast, the scene is indeed different, but the feelings partake more of horror than of wild delight.

CHARLES DARWIN
from *Voyage of the* Beagle

The Benefits of Not Travelling

I am willing to take your word for it that I shall realy oblige you by letting you know as soon as possible my safe passage over the water. I arriv'd this morning at Dover after being toss'd a whole night in the pacquet Boat in so violent a manner that the master, considering the weakness of his Vessel, thought it prudent to remove the mail, and gave us notice of the Danger. We call'd a little fisher boat, which could hardly make up to us, while all the people on board us were crying to Heaven, and 'tis hard to imagine one's selfe in a scene of greater Horror than on such an occasion; and yet, shall I own it to you? thô I was not at all willing to be drown'd, I could not forbear being entertain'd at the double distress of a fellow passenger. She was an English Lady that I had met at Calais, who desir'd me to let her go over with me in my Cabin. She had bought a fine point

head which she was contriving to conceal from the custom
house Officers. When the wind grew high and our little vessel
crack'd, she fell very heartily to her prayers and thought wholly
of her soul; when it seem'd to abate, she return'd to the worldly
care of her head dress, and address'd her selfe to me – Dear
madam, will you take care of this point? if it should be lost –
Ah Lord! we shall all be lost! Lord have mercy on my Soul –
pray, madam, take care of this head dress. – This easy transition
from her soul to her head dress, and the alternate Agonys that
both gave her, made it hard to determine which she thought of
greatest value. But, however, the scene was not so diverting but
I was glad to get rid of it and be thrown into the little boat, thô
with some hazard of breaking my neck. It brought me safe
hither, and I cannot help looking with partial Eyes on my Native
Land. That partiality was certainly given us by Nature to prevent
Rambling, the Effect of an Ambitious thirst after knowledge
which we are not form'd to Enjoy. All we get by it is a fruitless
Desire of mixing the different pleasures and conveniencies which
are given to Different parts of the World and cannot meet in
any one of them. After having read all that is to be found in the
Languages I am mistriss of, and having decaid my sight by
midnight studys, I envy the easy peace of mind of a ruddy
milk maid who, undisturb'd by doubt, hears the Sermon with
humility every Sunday, having not confus'd the sentiments of
Natural Duty in her head by the vain Enquirys of the Schools,
who may be more Learned, yet after all must remain as ignorant.
And, after having seen part of Asia and Africa and allmost made
the tour of Europe, I think the honest English Squire more
happy who verily beleives the Greek wines less delicious than
March beer, that the African fruits have not so fine a flavour as
golden Pipins, and the Becáfiguas of Italy are not so well tasted
as a rump of Beef, and that, in short, there is no perfect
Enjoyment of this Life out of Old England. I pray God I may

think so for the rest of my Life, and since I must be contented with our scanty allowance of Daylight, that I may forget the enlivening Sun of Constantinople.

LADY MARY WORTLEY MONTAGU

'Passage, immediate passage! . . .'

Passage, immediate passage! the blood burns in my veins!
Away O soul! hoist instantly the anchor!
Cut the hawsers – haul out – shake out every sail!
Have we not stood here like trees in the ground long enough?
Have we not grovel'd here long enough, eating and drinking
    like mere brutes?
Have we not darken'd and dazed ourselves with books long
    enough?

Sail forth – steer for the deep waters only,
Reckless O soul, exploring, I with thee, and thou with me,
For we are bound where mariner has not yet dared to go,
And we will risk the ship, ourselves and all.

O my brave soul!
O farther farther sail!
O daring joy, but safe! are they not all the seas of God?
O farther, farther, farther sail!

WALT WHITMAN
from 'A Passage to India'

Author Notes

The date given is that of the most recent Penguin edition.

MATTHEW ARNOLD (1822–88). 'Stanzas from Carnac' from *Selected Poems* (1994, 0 14 042376 1).

ELIZABETH BOWEN (1899–1973). 'The Pococks' Picnic' from *The Little Girls* (1982, 0 14 018305 1).

CHARLOTTE BRONTË (1816–55). 'Diving' from *The Penguin Book of Victorian Verse* (Allen Lane, 1997, 0 7139 9049 x) and 'The Voyage to Boue-Marine' from *Villette* (1979, 0 14 043118 7).

EDWARD ROBERT BULWER LYTTON (1831–91). 'Seaward' from *The Penguin Book of Victorian Verse* (Allen Lane, 1997, 0 7139 9049 x).

GEORGE GORDON, LORD BYRON (1788–1824). 'Now overhead a rainbow, bursting through' extracted from *Don Juan* (1973, 0 14 042216 1).

LEWIS CARROLL (1832–98). ' 'Tis the voice of the Lobster . . .' and 'The Walrus and the Carpenter' from *Alice's Adventures in Wonderland and Through the Looking-Glass* (1998, 0 14 043317 1).

GEORGE CHAPMAN (1560?–1634). 'The Tempest Raised by Poseidon' from *Homer in English* (1996, 0 14 044621 4).

GEOFFREY CHAUCER (1342?–1400). 'The Shipman' from 'The General Prologue' in *The Canterbury Tales: The First Fragment* (1996, 0 14 043409 7).

KATE CHOPIN (1851–1904). 'Grande Isle, Louisiana' from 'The Awakening' in *The Awakening and Selected Stories* (1984, 0 14 039022 7).

SAMUEL TAYLOR COLERIDGE (1772–1834). 'The breezes blew, the white foam flew' extracted from 'The Rime of the Ancyent Marinere (1798)' from *The Complete Poems* (1997, 0 14 042353 2).

WILKIE COLLINS (1824–89). 'A Wreck off the Isle of Man' from *Armadale* (1995, 0 14 043411 9).

JOSEPH CONRAD (1857–1924). 'The Thames Estuary' and 'The West African Coast' from *Heart of Darkness* (1995, 0 14 018652 2), 'A Typhoon in the South China Sea' from *Typhoon* in *Typhoon and Other Stories* (1990, 0 14 018257 8) and 'An Explosion in the Hold' and 'The Ship Rats' from *Youth* in *Youth and The End of the Tether* (1975, 0 14 018038 9).

WILLIAM COWPER (1731–1800). 'The Castaway', 'On the Loss of the Royal George' and 'Verses, Supposed to be Written by Alexander Selkirk' from *Selected Poems of Gray, Churchill and Cowper* (1998, 0 14 042401 6).

STEPHEN CRANE (1871–1900). 'In an Open Boat' from 'The Open Boat' in *The Red Badge of Courage and Other Stories* (1991, 0 14 039081 2).

RICHARD HENRY DANA, JR. (1815–82). 'An Albatross', 'Rounding Cape Horn' and 'Whales and Grampuses' from *Two Years before the Mast* (1986, 0 14 039008 1 o/p).

CHARLES DARWIN (1809–82). All extracts from *Voyage of the Beagle* (1989, 0 14 043268 x).

DANIEL DEFOE (1660–1731). 'The Footprint in the Sand' from *Robinson Crusoe* (1965, 0 14 043007 5).

CHARLES DICKENS (1812–70). 'An Atlantic Gale' from *American Notes for General Circulation* (1972, 0 14 043077 6) and 'A North Sea Storm' from *David Copperfield* (1997, 0 14 043494 1).

JOHN DONNE (1572–1631). Both poems from *The Complete English Poems* (1971, 0 14 042209 9).

GEORGE ELIOT (1819–80). 'On the Seashore' from 'The Ilfra-combe Journal' in *Selected Essays, Poems and Other Writings* (1990, 0 14 043148 9).

OLAUDAH EQUIANO (1735?–97). 'Taken into Slavery' from *The Interesting Narrative and Other Writings* (1995, 0 14 043485 2).

WILLIAM FALCONER (1732–69). 'Amid this fearful trance . . .' extracted from *The Shipwreck* from *Eighteenth-Century English Verse* (1973, 0 14 042169 6).

HENRY FIELDING (1707–54). 'Shipbuilding' from *The Journal of a Voyage to Lisbon* (1996, 0 14 043487 9).

WILLIAM EWART GLADSTONE (1809–98). 'Ode 1.14' from *Horace in English* (1996, 0 14 042387 7).

EDMUND GOSSE (1849–1928). 'Rock Pools' from *Father and Son* (1983, 0 14 043178 0).

RICHARD HAKLUYT (1552?–1616). All material from *Voyages and Discoveries* (1972, 0 14 043073 3).

THOMAS HARDY (1840–1928). Both poems from *Selected Poems* (1993, 0 14 043341 4).

LAFCADIO HEARN (1850–1904). 'Drifting' from *Writings from Japan* (1984, 0 14 043463 1).

LEIGH HUNT (1784–1859). 'The Fish, the Man, and the Spirit' from *The Penguin Book of Victorian Verse* (Allen Lane, 1997, 0 7139 9049 X).

SAMUEL JOHNSON (1709–84). 'The Isle of Muck' from *Journey to the Western Islands of Scotland* (1984, 0 14 043221 3).

JOHN KEATS (1795–1821). 'On First Looking into Chapman's Homer' from *The Complete Poems* (1973, 0 14 042210 2).

WILLIAM KETHE (?–1608?). Extract from Psalm 107 from *The*

Psalms in English (1996, 0 14 044618 4). The equally beautiful Authorized Version provided as a comparison.

D. H. LAWRENCE (1885–1930). 'By Steamer to Cagliari' from *Sea and Sardinia* in *D. H. Lawrence and Italy* (1997, 0 14 118030 7).

EDWARD LEAR (1812–88). 'The Jumblies' from *Victorian Verse* (1969, 0 14 042110 6).

EUGENE LEE-HAMILTON (1845–1907). 'Henry I to the Sea' from *Victorian Verse* (1969, 0 14 042110 6).

JACK LONDON (1876–1916). 'Shipwreck' from *The Sea-Wolf* in *The Sea-Wolf and Other Stories* (1989, 0 14 018357 4).

HENRY WADSWORTH LONGFELLOW (1807–82). Both poems from *Selected Poems* (1988, 0 14 039064 2 o/p).

ANDREW MARVELL (1621–78). 'Bermudas' from *The Complete Poems* (1972, 0 14 042213 7).

HERMAN MELVILLE (1819–91). 'Rock Rodondo' from 'Las Encantadas' in *Billy Budd, Sailor and Other Stories* (1967, 0 14 043029 6), 'The Fossil Whale' and 'Squid' from *Moby-Dick* (1992, 0 14 039084 7), 'A Narrow Escape' from *Redburn* (1976, 0 14 043105 5), 'The Enviable Isles' and 'The Maldive Shark' from *Nineteenth-Century American Poetry* (1996, 0 14 043587 5).

LADY MARY WORTLEY MONTAGU (1689–1762). 'The Benefits of Not Travelling' from *Selected Letters* (1997, 0 14 043490 9).

VLADIMIR NABOKOV (1899–1977). 'Biarritz' from 'First Love' in *Collected Stories* (1997, 0 14 118051 x) and *Nabokov's Dozen* (1960, 0 14 018167 9).

EDGAR ALLAN POE (1809–49). 'In the Southern Ocean' from *The Narrative of Arthur Gordon Pym of Nantucket* (1975, 0 14 043097 0).

ALEXANDER POPE (1688–1744). 'Ulysses under way after leaving Calypso' from *Homer in English* (1996, 0 14 044621 4).

WILLIAM CALDWELL ROSCOE (1823–59). 'By the Seashore' from *The Penguin Book of Victorian Verse* (Allen Lane, 1997, 0 7139 9049 x).

WILLIAM SHAKESPEARE (1564–1616). 'Thus with imagined wing . . .' from *Henry V* (1968, 0 14 070708 5), 'In sooth I know not why I am so sad' from *The Merchant of Venice* (1967, 0 14 070706 9), 'Full fathom five thy father lies' and 'If by your art, my dearest father . . .' from *The Tempest* (1968, 0 14 070713 1).

MARY SHELLEY (1797–1851). 'The Monster Pursued' from *Frankenstein* (1992, 0 14 043362 7).

TOBIAS SMOLLETT (1721–71). 'The Ever Memorable Expedition to Carthagena' from *Roderick Random* (1995, 0 14 043332 5).

ROBERT LOUIS STEVENSON (1850–94). 'The Pacific Atoll' from *The Ebb-Tide* in *Dr Jekyll and Mr Hyde and Other Stories* (1979, 0 14 043117 9), 'The Loss of the Brig' from *Kidnapped* (1994, 0 14 043401 1) and 'The Light-Keeper' from *The Penguin Book of Victorian Verse* (Allen Lane, 1997, 0 7139 9049 x).

BRAM STOKER (1847–1912). 'Log of the *Demeter*' from *Dracula* (1993, 0 14 043381 3).

JONATHAN SWIFT (1667–1745). 'Castaway' from *Gulliver's Travels* (1967, 0 14 043022 9).

ALFRED LORD TENNYSON (1809–92). All poems from *Selected Poems* (1991, 0 14 044545 5).

CHARLES TENNYSON TURNER (1808–79). 'The Buoy-Bell' from *Victorian Verse* (1969, 0 14 042110 6).

WILLIAM MAKEPEACE THACKERAY (1811–63). 'The Three

Sailors [Little Billee]' from *The Penguin Book of Victorian Verse* (Allen Lane, 1997, 0 7139 9049 x).

EDWARD THOMPSON (1739?–86). Not actually from a Penguin Classic at all – but such a fine and rare insight into ordinary service life that it had to be included. Extract from 'An Humble Wish. Off Porto-Santo, March 29, 1779' from *The New Oxford Book of Eighteenth-Century Verse*, chosen and edited by Roger Lonsdale (OUP, 1984).

EVELYN WAUGH (1903–66). 'Voyage to Ishmaelia' from *Scoop* (1943, 0 14 018248 9).

WALT WHITMAN (1819–92). All poems from *The Complete Poems* (1975, 0 14 042222 6).

MARY WOLLSTONECRAFT (1759–97). 'In the Kattegat' from *A Short Residence in Sweden, Norway, and Denmark* (1987, 0 14 043269 8).

VIRGINIA WOOLF (1882–1941). 'The Docks of London' from *The Crowded Dance of Modern Life* (1993, 0 14 018564 x).

WILLIAM WORDSWORTH (1770–1850). All poems from *Selected Poems* (1994, 0 14 042375 3).

Acknowledgements

The publishers gratefully acknowledge the following for permission to reprint copyright material in this volume:

ELIZABETH BOWEN: for 'The Pococks' Picnic' from *The Little Girls* (Penguin Books, 1982), copyright © Elizabeth Bowen, 1963, 1964, reproduced by permission of Curtis Brown, London, and Alfred A. Knopf Inc.; EDMUND GOSSE: for 'Rock Pools' from *Father and Son* (Penguin Books, 1983), reprinted by kind permission of Jennifer Gosse; THOMAS HARDY: for 'The Convergence of the Twain' and 'Beeny Cliff' from *Selected Poems* (Penguin Books, 1993), reprinted by permission of Macmillan Publishers Ltd; D. H. LAWRENCE: for 'By Steamer to Cagliari' from *Sea and Sardinia* (Penguin Books, 1997), reprinted by permission of Laurence Pollinger Ltd and the Estate of Frieda Lawrence Ravagli; VLADIMIR NABOKOV: for 'Biarritz' from 'First Love' in *Collected Stories* (Penguin Books, 1997), reprinted by permission of Weidenfeld & Nicolson Ltd and Smith/Skolnik Literary Management; EVELYN WAUGH: for 'Voyage to Ishmaelia' from *Scoop* (Penguin Books, 1943), reprinted by permission of The Peters Fraser & Dunlop Group Ltd; VIRGINIA WOOLF: for 'The Docks of London' from *The Crowded Dance of Modern Life* (Penguin Books, 1993), reprinted by permission of The Society of Authors as the Literary Representative of the Estate of Virginia Woolf; Extracts from the Authorized Version of the Bible (the King James Bible), the rights in which are vested in the Crown, are reproduced by permission of the Crown's Patentee, Cambridge University Press.

The Penguin Classics and Twentieth-Century Classics series now include over 1,400 titles, encompassing the very best writing from around the world, an extraordinary wealth of literature and non-fiction from ancient civilizations to the present day.

With *Sea Longing*, we are delighted to be able to offer you £1 off the Penguin Black Classic or Penguin Twentieth-Century Classic of your choice by using the voucher below.

TO THE CUSTOMER:

To obtain £1 off, please fill in the details below and hand in the completed voucher to the cashier when purchasing any Penguin Black Classic or Penguin Twentieth-Century Classic.

*Name*_____

Address _____

_____

Postcode _____

Title purchased _____

This voucher is only valid against the purchase of a Penguin Black Classic or Penguin Twentieth-Century Classic. The offer does not apply to audio books. This offer ends on 31st December 1998 and is only valid in the UK and Republic of Ireland.

All information will be treated in confidence and will not be passed on to any other organization.

☐ Tick here if you do not wish to receive any further information from Penguin Books.

TO THE BOOKSHOP - BOOKSHOP USE ONLY:

Please accept this voucher as £1 discount against the purchase of any Penguin Black Classic or Penguin Twentieth-Century Classic, made no later than 31st December 1998. This offer does not apply to audio books.

Name _____ *Store and branch* _____

Address _____

_____ *Postcode* _____

*Penguin account number*_____

Signature _____

To receive credit on your account, please return completed vouchers to:
Sea Longing Voucher Offer,
Penguin Press Marketing Department, 27 Wrights Lane, London W8 5TZ.

Incomplete vouchers or those returned after 31st January 1999 will not be accepted for credit. If you have a query on your account please telephone your customer services coordinator.

READ MORE IN PENGUIN

In every corner of the world, on every subject under the sun, Penguin represents quality and variety – the very best in publishing today.

For complete information about books available from Penguin – including Puffins, Penguin Classics and Arkana – and how to order them, write to us at the appropriate address below. Please note that for copyright reasons the selection of books varies from country to country.

In the United Kingdom: Please write to *Dept. EP, Penguin Books Ltd, Bath Road, Harmondsworth, West Drayton, Middlesex UB7 0DA*

In the United States: Please write to *Consumer Sales, Penguin Putnam Inc., P.O. Box 999, Dept. 17109, Bergenfield, New Jersey 07621-0120.* VISA and MasterCard holders call 1-800-253-6476 to order Penguin titles

In Canada: Please write to *Penguin Books Canada Ltd, 10 Alcorn Avenue, Suite 300, Toronto, Ontario M4V 3B2*

In Australia: Please write to *Penguin Books Australia Ltd, P.O. Box 257, Ringwood, Victoria 3134*

In New Zealand: Please write to *Penguin Books (NZ) Ltd, Private Bag 102902, North Shore Mail Centre, Auckland 10*

In India: Please write to *Penguin Books India Pvt Ltd, 210 Chiranjiv Tower, 43 Nehru Place, New Delhi 110 019*

In the Netherlands: Please write to *Penguin Books Netherlands bv, Postbus 3507, NL-1001 AH Amsterdam*

In Germany: Please write to *Penguin Books Deutschland GmbH, Metzlerstrasse 26, 60594 Frankfurt am Main*

In Spain: Please write to *Penguin Books S. A., Bravo Murillo 19, 1° B, 28015 Madrid*

In Italy: Please write to *Penguin Italia s.r.l., Via Benedetto Croce 2, 20094 Corsico, Milano*

In France: Please write to *Penguin France, Le Carré Wilson, 62 rue Benjamin Baillaud, 31500 Toulouse*

In Japan: Please write to *Penguin Books Japan Ltd, Kaneko Building, 2-3-25 Koraku, Bunkyo-Ku, Tokyo 112*

In South Africa: Please write to *Penguin Books South Africa (Pty) Ltd, Private Bag X14, Parkview, 2122 Johannesburg*

READ MORE IN PENGUIN

A CHOICE OF CLASSICS

Kate Chopin	**The Awakening and Selected Stories**
	A Vocation and a Voice
James Fenimore Cooper	**The Last of the Mohicans**
	The American Democrat
Stephen Crane	**The Red Badge of Courage**
Frederick Douglass	**Narrative of the Life of Frederick Douglass, An American Slave**
Ralph Waldo Emerson	**Selected Essays**
Nathaniel Hawthorne	**The Blithedale Romance**
	The House of the Seven Gables
	The Scarlet Letter and Selected Tales
William Dean Howells	**The Rise of Silas Lapham**
Henry James	**The Ambassadors**
	The American Scene
	The Aspern Papers/The Turn of the Screw
	The Awkward Age
	The Bostonians
	The Critical Muse
	Daisy Miller
	The Europeans
	The Figure in the Carpet
	The Golden Bowl
	An International Episode
	The Jolly Corner and Other Tales
	A Landscape Painter and Other Tales
	The Portrait of a Lady
	The Princess Casamassima
	Roderick Hudson
	The Sacred Fount
	The Spoils of Poynton
	The Tragic Muse
	Washington Square
	What Maisie Knew
	The Wings of the Dove

READ MORE IN PENGUIN

A CHOICE OF CLASSICS

READ MORE IN PENGUIN

A SELECTION OF POETRY

American Verse
British Poetry since 1945
Caribbean Verse in English
Chinese Love Poetry
A Choice of Comic and Curious Verse
Contemporary American Poetry
Contemporary British Poetry
Contemporary Irish Poetry
English Poetry 1918–60
English Romantic Verse
English Verse
First World War Poetry
German Verse
Greek Verse
Homosexual Verse
Imagist Poetry
Irish Verse
Japanese Verse
The Metaphysical Poets
Modern African Poetry
New Poetry
Poetry of the Thirties
Scottish Verse
Surrealist Poetry in English
Spanish Verse
Victorian Verse
Women Poets
Zen Poetry